PRIMARY MATHEMATICS

TEXTBOOK 5B

Common Core Edition

SINGAPORE MATH® PROGRAM

Marshall Cavendish
Education

US Distributor

SM Singapore Math Inc.®

W9-BMV-053

BLANK

Original edition published under the title Primary Mathematics Textbook 5B
© 1981 Curriculum Planning & Development Division, Ministry of Education, Singapore
Published by Times Media Private Limited

This edition © 2014 Marshall Cavendish Education Pte Ltd
(Formerly known as Marshall Cavendish International (Singapore) Private Limited)

Published by Marshall Cavendish Education
Times Centre, 1 New Industrial Road, Singapore 536196
Customer Service Hotline: (65) 6213 9444
US Office Tel: (1-914) 332 8888 | Fax: (1-914) 332 8882
E-mail: tmesales@mceducation.com
Website: www.mceducation.com

Distributed by
Singapore Math Inc.®
19535 SW 129th Avenue
Tualatin, OR 97062, U.S.A.
Tel: (503) 557 8100
Website: www.singaporemath.com

First published 2014
Reprinted 2014

Primary Mathematics (Common Core Edition) Textbook 5B
ISBN 978-981-01-9838-1

Printed in Malaysia

Primary Mathematics (Common Core Edition) is adapted from Primary Mathematics Textbook 5B (3rd Edition),
originally developed by the Ministry of Education, Singapore. This edition contains new content developed by
Marshall Cavendish Education Pte Ltd, which is not attributable to the Ministry of Education, Singapore.

We would like to acknowledge the contributions by:

The Project Team from the Ministry of Education, Singapore that developed the original Singapore edition
Project Director: Dr Kho Tek Hong
Team Members: Hector Chee Kum Hoong, Liang Hin Hoon, Lim Eng Tann, Ng Siew Lee, Rosalind Lim Hui Cheng,
Ng Hwee Wan

Primary Mathematics (Common Core Edition)
Richard Askey, Emeritus Professor of Mathematics from University of Wisconsin, Madison
Jennifer Kempe, Curriculum Advisor from Singapore Math Inc.®

PREFACE

PRIMARY MATHEMATICS Common Core Edition is a complete program from Marshall Cavendish Education, the publisher of Singapore's successful *Primary Mathematics* series. Newly adapted to align with the Common Core State Standards for mathematics, the program aims to equip students with sound concept development, critical thinking and efficient problem-solving skills.

Mathematical concepts are introduced in the opening pages and taught to mastery through specific learning tasks that allow for immediate assessment and consolidation.

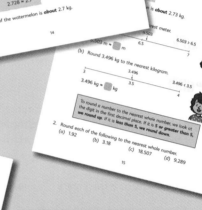

The **modeling method** enables students to visualize and solve mathematical problems quickly and efficiently.

The **Concrete → Pictorial → Abstract** approach enables students to encounter math in a meaningful way and translate mathematical skills from the concrete to the abstract.

The **pencil icon** Exercise 18, pages 18-20 provides quick and easy reference from the Textbook to the relevant Workbook pages. The **direct correlation** of the Workbook to the Textbook facilitates focused review and evaluation.

New mathematical concepts are introduced through a **spiral progression** that builds on concepts already taught and mastered.

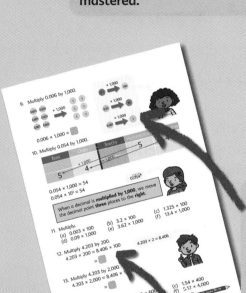

Metacognition is employed as a strategy for learners to monitor their thinking processes in problem solving. Speech and thought bubbles provide guidance through the thought processes, making even the most challenging problems accessible to students.

The color patch is used to invite active student participation and to facilitate lively discussion about the mathematical concepts taught.

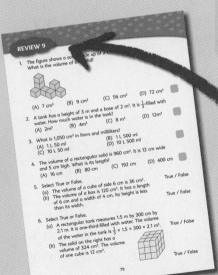

Regular **reviews** in the Textbook provide consolidation of concepts learned.

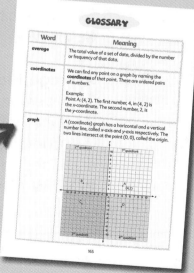

The **glossary** effectively combines pictorial representation with simple mathematical definitions to provide a comprehensive reference guide for students.

CONTENTS

7 DECIMALS

1 Tenths, Hundredths, and Thousandths

John jumped a distance of 0.83 m in the standing broad jump.

Divide 1 m into 10 equal parts.
Each part is 0.1 m.
8 parts make up 0.8 m.

0.83 m is 0.03 m
more than 0.8 m.

1 m

0.8 m

0.1 m

0.03 m

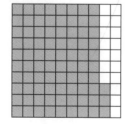

Divide 0.1 m into 10 equal parts.
Each part is 0.01 m.
3 parts make up 0.03 m.

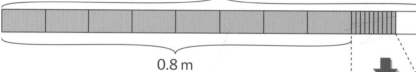

$$0.83 = 0.8 + 0.03$$

0.83 is 8 tenths and 3 hundredths.
0.83 is also 83 hundredths.

$$0.83 = \frac{8}{10} + \frac{3}{100} = \frac{83}{100}$$

$$0.83 = 8 \div 10 + 3 \div 10^2$$

$$= 8 \times \frac{1}{10} + 3 \times \frac{1}{10^2}$$

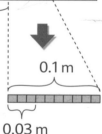

1.

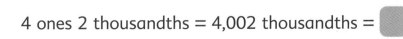

1 → 0.1 0.1 0.1 0.1 0.1 / 0.1 0.1 0.1 0.1 0.1

1 one = 10 tenths

0.1 → 0.01 0.01 0.01 0.01 0.01 / 0.01 0.01 0.01 0.01 0.01

1 tenth = 10 hundredths

Write a decimal for each of the following.

(a) 0.1 0.1 0.1   0.01 0.01 0.01 0.01 0.01

3 tenths 5 hundredths = 35 hundredths = ☐

(b) 1 1 1   0.1 0.1 0.1 0.1 0.1   0.1 0.1

3 ones 7 tenths = 37 tenths = ☐

(c) 1 1   0.01 0.01 0.01 0.01

2 ones 4 hundredths = 204 hundredths = ☐

2.

0.01 → 0.001 0.001 0.001 0.001 0.001 / 0.001 0.001 0.001 0.001 0.001

1 hundredth = 10 thousandths

Write a decimal for each of the following.

(a) 0.01 0.01   0.001 0.001 0.001 0.001

2 hundredths 4 thousandths = 24 thousandths = ☐

(b) 0.1 0.1 0.1   0.01   0.001 0.001 0.001 0.001 0.001

3 tenths 1 hundredth 5 thousandths = 315 thousandths = ☐

(c) 1 1 1 1   0.001 0.001

4 ones 2 thousandths = 4,002 thousandths = ☐

3.

20.435 = 2 tens 4 tenths 3 hundredths 5 thousandths
20.435 has 3 decimal places.
(a) The digit 5 is in the thousandths place. What is its value?
(b) What is the value of each of the other digits?

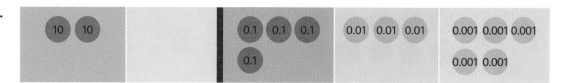

The **tenths place, hundredths place,** and **thousandths place** are called **decimal places**.

Read 20.435 as twenty point four three five, or as twenty and four hundred and thirty-five thousandths.

4. (a) What is 0.01 more than 5.62?
    (b) What is 0.01 less than 5.62?
    (c) What is 0.001 more than 4.536?
    (d) What is 0.001 less than 4.536?

5. What is the missing number in each ?

    (a) 27.148 is   more than 27

    (b) 27.148 is   more than 27.1

    (c) 27.148 is   more than 27.14

6. What is the missing number in each ?

    (a) 30.134 = 30 +   + 0.03 + 0.004

    (b) 4.506 = 4 + 0.5 +

    (c) 30.023 =   + 0.023

7. There are 34 tenths in 3.465.

   (a) How many hundredths are in 3.465?

   (b) How many thousandths are in 3.465?

8. What is the missing number in each ?

   (a) $300 = 3 \times 100$

   (b) $60 = 6 \times$ ▢

   (c) $4 = 4 \times$ ▢

   (d) $0.7 = 7 \times \frac{1}{10}$

   (e) $0.05 = 5 \times \frac{1}{▢}$

   (f) $0.002 = 2 \times \frac{1}{▢}$

   (g) $364.752 = 3 \times 100 + 6 \times$ ▢ $+ 4 \times$ ▢ $+ 0.7 \times \frac{1}{▢} +$

   $5 \times \frac{1}{▢} + 2 \times \frac{1}{▢}$

9. Write the following as a decimal.

   $5 \times \frac{1}{10^3} = \frac{5}{1,000}$

   $=$ ▢

10. Write each of the following as a decimal.

   (a) $3 \times 10^3 + 5 \times 10^2 + 1 \times 10 + 4 + 2 \times \frac{1}{10} + 1 \times \frac{1}{10^2} + 5 \times \frac{1}{10^3}$

   (b) $5 \times 10^2 + 3 + 8 \times \frac{1}{10} + 8 \times \frac{1}{10^2}$

   (c) $8 \times 10^3 + 2 \times 10 + 3 \times \frac{1}{10^2}$

   (d) $8 \times 10^2 + 42 \times \frac{1}{10^3}$

   (e) $10^2 + 6 \times \frac{1}{10^2}$

   Exercise 1, pages 5—6

11. What number does each letter represent?

   (a)

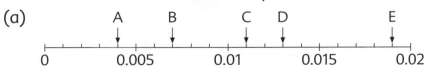

11

(b)

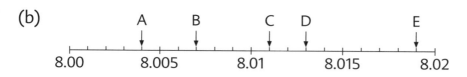

(c)

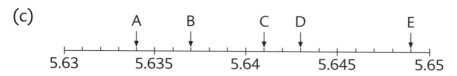

12. (a) Which is greater, 42.54 or 42.326?

Tens	Ones	•	Tenths	Hundredths	Thousandths
4	2		5	4	0
4	2		3	2	6

   Which sign goes in the ⬤, > or < ?

   42.54 ⬤ 42.326

(b) Which is smaller, 63.182 or 63.187?

Tens	Ones	•	Tenths	Hundredths	Thousandths
6	3		1	8	2
6	3		1	8	7

   Which sign goes in the ⬤, > or < ?

   63.182 ⬤ 63.187

13. Copy and write >, <, or = in each ⬤.

   (a) 4.6 ⬤ 4.58   (b) 26.98 ⬤ 27.2

   (c) 1.008 ⬤ 1.1   (d) 6.328 ⬤ 6.325

   (e) 12.439 ⬤ 12.34   (f) 15.004 ⬤ 15.04

14. Arrange the numbers in decreasing order.
    (a) 0.32, 0.302, 0.032, 3.02
    (b) 2.139, 2.628, 2.045, 2.189

15. Arrange the numbers in increasing order.
    (a) 5.8, 0.538, 0.83, 3.58
    (b) 9.047, 9.076, 9.074, 9.067

16. Express 0.052 as a fraction in its simplest form.

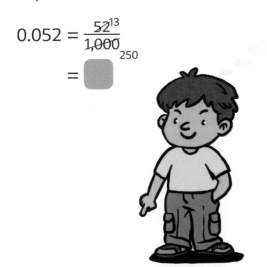

$$0.052 = \frac{52^{13}}{1{,}000_{250}}$$

$$= \boxed{}$$

0.052 = 52 thousandths

$$= \frac{52}{1{,}000}$$

The simplest form of $\frac{52}{1{,}000}$ is $\frac{13}{250}$.

17. Express each decimal as a fraction in its simplest form.
    (a) 0.5   (b) 0.08   (c) 0.25
    (d) 0.48   (e) 0.006   (f) 0.024
    (g) 0.345   (h) 0.528

18. Express 2.045 as a fraction in its simplest form.

$$2.045 = 2\frac{45}{1{,}000}$$

$$= \boxed{}$$

19. Express each decimal as a fraction in its simplest form.
    (a) 2.6   (b) 3.2   (c) 1.25
    (d) 6.05   (e) 3.002   (f) 2.075
    (g) 2.408   (h) 4.125

Exercise 2, page 7

❷ Approximation

The mass of the watermelon is 2.728 kg.

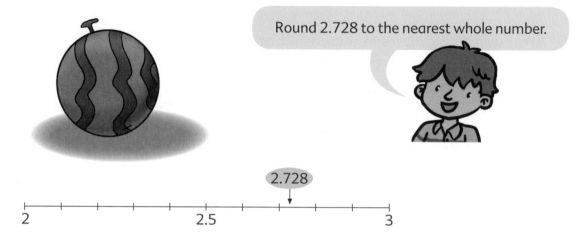

Round 2.728 to the nearest whole number.

2.728 is more than halfway between 2 and 3. It is rounded to 3.

We write:

$$2.728 \approx 3$$

The mass of the watermelon is **about** 3 kg.

Round 2.728 to 1 decimal place.

2.728 is less than halfway between 2.7 and 2.8. It is rounded to 2.7.

We write:

$$2.728 \approx 2.7$$

The mass of the watermelon is **about** 2.7 kg.

Round 2.728 to 2 decimal places.

2.728

2.72   2.725   2.73

2.728 is more than halfway between 2.72 and 2.73.
It is rounded to 2.73.

We write: | 2.728 ≈ 2.73 |

The mass of the watermelon is **about** 2.73 kg.

1. (a) Round 6.503 m to the nearest meter.

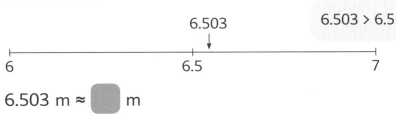

6.503

6.503 > 6.5

6   6.5   7

6.503 m ≈ ⬜ m

(b) Round 3.496 kg to the nearest kilogram.

3.496

3.496 < 3.5

3   3.5   4

3.496 kg ≈ ⬜ kg

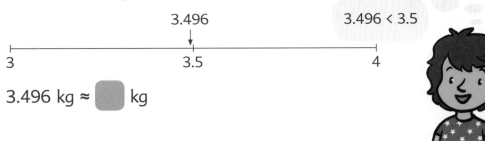

To round a number to the nearest whole number, we look at
the digit in the first decimal place. If it is **5 or greater than 5,
we round up**. If it is **less than 5, we round down**.

2. Round each of the following to the nearest whole number.
   (a) 1.92   (b) 3.18   (c) 18.507   (d) 9.289

3.

14.32 is [ ] when rounded to 1 decimal place.

14.35 is [ ] when rounded to 1 decimal place.

14.382 is [ ] when rounded to 1 decimal place.

> To round a number to the nearest 1 decimal place, we look at the digit in the second decimal place. If it is **5 or greater than 5, we round up**. If it is **less than 5, we round down**.

4. Round each of the following to 1 decimal place.
   (a) 6.09　　　(b) 29.92　　　(c) 40.752　　　(d) 17.648

5.

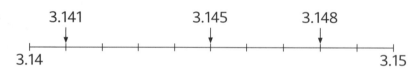

3.148 is [ ] when rounded to 2 decimal places.

3.141 is [ ] when rounded to 2 decimal places.

3.145 is [ ] when rounded to 2 decimal places.

> To round a number to the nearest 2 decimal places, we look at the digit in the third decimal place. If it is **5 or greater than 5, we round up**. If it is **less than 5, we round down**.

6. Round each of the following to 2 decimal places.
   (a) 5.168　　　(b) 8.044　　　(c) 10.805　　　(d) 23.718

Exercise 3, page 8

❸ Add and Subtract Decimals

Add 2.63 and 3.84.

```
   2 . 6 3
+  3 . 8 4
```

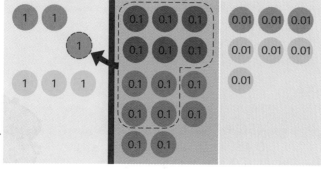

There are 14 tenths in all.
Rename 10 tenths as 1.
14 tenths = 1 one 4 tenths.

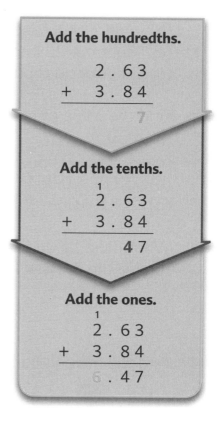

Add the hundredths.

```
   2 . 6 3
+  3 . 8 4
         7
```

Add the tenths.

```
     1
   2 . 6 3
+  3 . 8 4
       4 7
```

Add the ones.

```
     1
   2 . 6 3
+  3 . 8 4
   6 . 4 7
```

Subtract 2.53 from 4.27.

```
   4 . 2 7
-  2 . 5 3
```

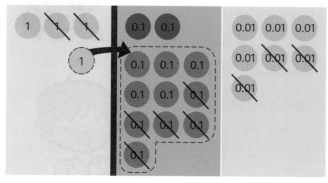

There are not enough tenths to subtract
5 tenths.
Rename 1 one as 10 tenths. Then subtract.
4 ones 2 tenths = 3 ones 12 tenths.

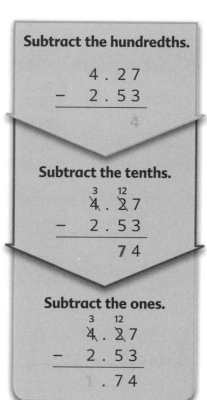

Subtract the hundredths.

```
   4 . 2 7
-  2 . 5 3
         4
```

Subtract the tenths.

```
   3    12
   4 . 2 7
-  2 . 5 3
       7 4
```

Subtract the ones.

```
   3    12
   4 . 2 7
-  2 . 5 3
   1 . 7 4
```

1. What is the answer?
    (a) Add 4 tenths to 4.536.
    (b) Add 3 thousandths to 4.536.
    (c) Subtract 2 hundredths from 4.536.
    (d) Subtract 6 thousandths from 4.536.

2. Find the value of each of the following.
    (a) 2.465 + 0.2   (b) 3.842 − 0.6
    (c) 1.246 + 0.03   (d) 4.567 − 0.04
    (e) 3.125 + 0.004   (f) 2.043 − 0.002
    (g) 6.1 + 0.006   (h) 5.208 − 0.008

3. What must be added to 0.456
   to give the answer 1?

   456 + 544 = 1,000
   0.456 + 0.544 = 1
   1 − 0.456 = 0.544

4. Find the missing number.

    (a) 1 − ⬜ = 0.46   (b) 1 − ⬜ = 0.31   (c) 1 − 0.069 = ⬜

    (d) 2 − 1.069 = ⬜   (e) 3.42 + ⬜ = 5   (f) 12 − 11.111 = ⬜

5. Estimate. Then find the value of 1.3 + 2.93.

    1.3 + 2.93 ≈ ⬜   1.3 + 2.93 ≈ 1 + 3

    1.3 + 2.93 = ⬜

6. Estimate. Then find the value of 3.2 − 0.38.

    3.2 − 0.38 ≈ ⬜   3.2 − 0.38 ≈ 3 − 0.4

    3.2 − 0.38 = ⬜

7. Estimate. Then find the value of each of the following.
    (a) 2.4 + 3.75   (b) 8.61 + 6.2   (c) 48.7 + 20.68
    (d) 9.82 − 7.93   (e) 10.3 − 5.19   (f) 63.12 − 5.9

18

Exercise 4, page 9

④ Multiply and Divide Decimals by a 1-Digit Whole Number

Multiply 0.03 by 2.

$$\begin{array}{r} 0.03 \\ \times \quad 2 \\ \hline 0.06 \end{array}$$

3 hundredths × 2
= 6 hundredths
= 0.06

Multiply 0.6 by 2.

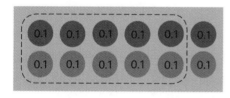 

$$\begin{array}{r} 0.6 \\ \times \quad 2 \\ \hline 1.2 \end{array}$$

6 tenths × 2
= 12 tenths
= 1 one 2 tenths
= 1.2

Multiply 4.63 by 2.

$$4.63 \times 2$$

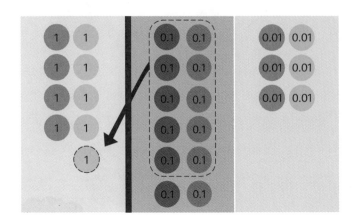

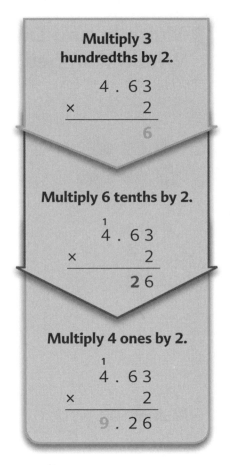

Multiply 3 hundredths by 2.

$$
\begin{array}{r}
4.63 \\
\times \quad 2 \\
\hline
6
\end{array}
$$

Multiply 6 tenths by 2.

$$
\begin{array}{r}
{}^{1} \\
4.63 \\
\times \quad 2 \\
\hline
26
\end{array}
$$

Multiply 4 ones by 2.

$$
\begin{array}{r}
{}^{1} \\
4.63 \\
\times \quad 2 \\
\hline
9.26
\end{array}
$$

We can multiply 4.63 by 2 the same way we multiply 463 by 2.

$463 \times 2 = 926$

$4.63 \times 2 = 463$ hundredths $\times 2$
$= 926$ hundredths
$= 9.26$

1. Find the product of each of the following.
   (a) 7×3
   (b) 0.7×3
   (c) 0.07×3
   (d) 0.007×3
   (e) 14×6
   (f) 1.4×6
   (g) 0.14×6
   (h) 0.014×6

2. Find the product of each of the following.
   (a) 542 × 5   (b) 54.2 × 5   (c) 0.542 × 5
   (d) 896 × 8   (e) 89.6 × 8   (f) 8.96 × 8

3. Estimate. Then find the value of 2.08 × 3.

   2.08 × 3 ≈ 2 × 3 =

   2.08 × 3 =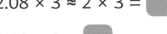

4. Estimate. Then find the value of each of the following.
   (a) 4.82 × 3   (b) 3.63 × 6   (c) 9 × 43.25
   (d) 9.348 × 5   (e) 5.046 × 7   (f) 27.08 × 4

 Exercise 5, pages 10–11

5. Divide 0.006 by 2.

   6 thousandths ÷ 2
   = 3 thousandths

   0.006 ÷ 2 =

6. Divide 0.15 by 3.

   0.15 ÷ 3 =

   15 hundredths ÷ 3
   = 5 hundredths

```
     0 . 0 5
  3 ) 0 . 1 5
       1 5
       ─────
        0
```

   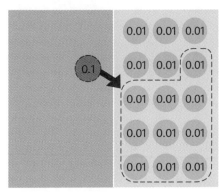

7. Divide 0.2 by 4.

20 hundredths ÷ 4
= 5 hundredths

$0.2 ÷ 4 = 0.20 ÷ 4$

$\quad = \boxed{}$

8. Find the value of each of the following.
   (a) $40 ÷ 8$ (b) $4 ÷ 8$
   (c) $0.4 ÷ 8$ (d) $0.04 ÷ 8$
   (e) $0.42 ÷ 7$ (f) $0.042 ÷ 7$
   (g) $8.1 ÷ 9$ (h) $0.081 ÷ 9$

9. Divide 8.1 by 6.

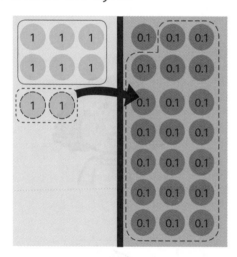

$8 ÷ 6 = 1$ with 2 ones remaining.
Rename 2 ones as 20 tenths.

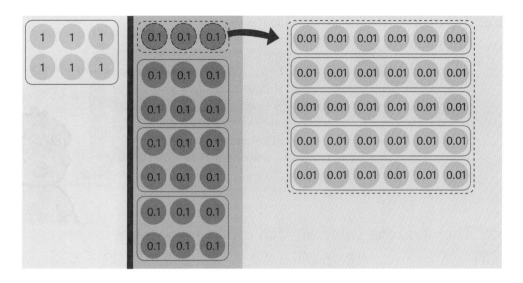

There are 21 tenths in all.
$21 \div 6 = 3$ tenths with 3 tenths remaining.
Rename 3 tenths as 30 hundredths.
30 hundredths $\div 6 = 5$ hundredths

$8.1 \div 6 = 1.35$

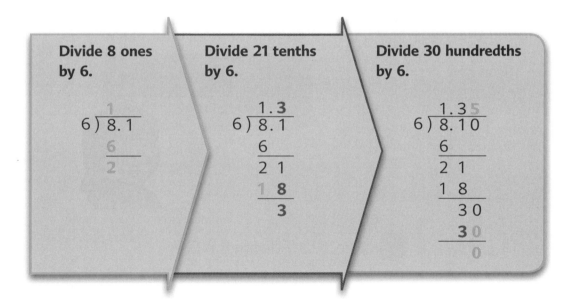

Divide 8 ones by 6.	Divide 21 tenths by 6.	Divide 30 hundredths by 6.

We can divide 8.1 by 6 the same way we divide 810 by 6.

$810 \div 6 = 135$

$$8.1 \div 6 = 810 \text{ hundredths} \div 6$$
$$= 135 \text{ hundredths}$$
$$= 1.35$$

23

10. Estimate. Then find the value of 3.61 ÷ 5.

$3.61 ÷ 5 ≈ 3.5 ÷ 5 =$

$3.61 ÷ 5 =$

I can estimate the problem this way:
3 is a little more than half of 5. The answer will be a little more than 0.5.

11. Estimate. Then find the value of each of the following.
   (a) 22.11 ÷ 3
   (b) 5.04 ÷ 7
   (c) 27.08 ÷ 4
   (d) 1.14 ÷ 6
   (e) 8.12 ÷ 8
   (f) 0.816 ÷ 3

Exercise 6, pages 12–13

12. (a) Estimate the value of 21.36 ÷ 9.

   $21.36 ÷ 9 ≈ 18 ÷ 9$

   $=$

   (b) Find the value of 21.36 ÷ 9 correct to 1 decimal place.

```
        2 . 3 7 ≈ 2.4
    9 ) 2 1 . 3 6
        1 8
        ‾‾‾
          3 3
          2 7
        ‾‾‾‾
            6 6
            6 3
          ‾‾‾‾
              3
```

Divide to 2 decimal places. Then round the answer to 1 decimal place.

The answer is  correct to 1 decimal place.

24

13. Find the value of each of the following correct to 1 decimal place.
    (a) 21.2 ÷ 3   (b) 47.2 ÷ 9   (c) 29.6 ÷ 7
    (d) 3.36 ÷ 4   (e) 26.43 ÷ 6   (f) 9.43 ÷ 8

14. (a) Estimate the value of 24.65 ÷ 8.

    24.65 ÷ 8 ≈ 24 ÷ 8
              =

    The estimated value is ⬜.

    (b) Find the value of 24.65 ÷ 8 correct to 2 decimal places.

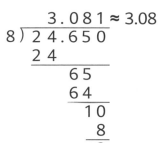

    Divide to 3 decimal places.
    Then round the answer to
    2 decimal places.

    The answer is ⬜ correct to 2 decimal places.

15. Find the value of each of the following correct to 2 decimal places.
    (a) 0.77 ÷ 9   (b) 62.7 ÷ 7   (c) 9.65 ÷ 8
    (d) 41.51 ÷ 6   (e) 27.69 ÷ 4   (f) 20.93 ÷ 3

Exercise 7, page 14

16. Express $\frac{3}{4}$ as a decimal.

Method 1:

$$\frac{3}{4} = \frac{75}{100} = \boxed{}$$

with ×25 above and ×25 below

Method 2:

$$\frac{3}{4} = 3 ÷ 4 = \boxed{}$$

17. Express $\frac{1}{8}$ as a decimal.　　$\frac{1}{8} = 1 \div 8$

18. Express $3\frac{2}{5}$ as a decimal.

$3\frac{2}{5} = 3 + 0.4$

19. Express each fraction as a decimal.

(a) $2\frac{1}{4}$ 　　 (b) $4\frac{3}{8}$ 　　 (c) $1\frac{4}{5}$ 　　 (d) $6\frac{7}{8}$

20. Arrange the numbers in increasing order.

$\frac{5}{8}$, 0.652, 2, 0.6

21. (a) Express $\frac{5}{9}$ as a decimal correct to 1 decimal place.

$$\begin{array}{r} 0.55 \approx 0.6 \\ 9\overline{)5.00} \\ 4\ 5 \\ \hline 5\ 0 \\ 4\ 5 \\ \hline 5 \end{array}$$

$\frac{5}{9} = 5 \div 9 \approx 0.6$

OR

$\frac{5}{9} = 5 \div 9 = 0.6$ (correct to 1 decimal place)

The answer is ▢ correct to 1 decimal place.

(b) Express $3\frac{5}{9}$ as a decimal correct to 1 decimal place.

$3\frac{5}{9} \approx 3 + 0.6 = 3.6$

The answer is ▢ correct to 1 decimal place.

22. Express each fraction as a decimal correct to 1 decimal place.

(a) $\frac{3}{4}$

(b) $\frac{4}{7}$

(c) $\frac{4}{9}$

(d) $\frac{5}{6}$

(e) $2\frac{2}{3}$

(f) $4\frac{6}{7}$

(g) $3\frac{1}{6}$

(h) $1\frac{8}{9}$

23. Express $4\frac{2}{3}$ as a decimal correct to 2 decimal places.

$$
\begin{array}{r}
0.666 \approx 0.67 \\
3\overline{)2.000} \\
1\ 8 \\
\hline
2\ 0 \\
1\ 8 \\
\hline
2\ 0 \\
1\ 8 \\
\hline
2
\end{array}
$$

$\frac{2}{3} \approx$ ⬜

$4\frac{2}{3} \approx$ ⬜

OR

$4\frac{2}{3} =$ ⬜ (correct to 2 decimal places)

The answer is ⬜ correct to 2 decimal places.

24. Express each fraction as a decimal correct to 2 decimal places.

(a) $\frac{3}{7}$

(b) $\frac{5}{8}$

(c) $\frac{2}{9}$

(d) $\frac{1}{6}$

(e) $5\frac{7}{9}$

(f) $1\frac{1}{3}$

(g) $4\frac{5}{7}$

(h) $8\frac{3}{8}$

(i) $\frac{1}{8}$

(j) $\frac{4}{7}$

(k) $2\frac{5}{9}$

(l) $5\frac{2}{3}$

Exercise 8, pages 15–16

⑤ Multiplication by Tens, Hundreds, or Thousands

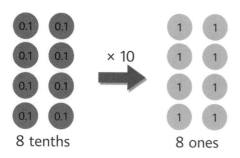

8 tenths → 8 ones

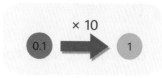

0.8 × 10 = 8

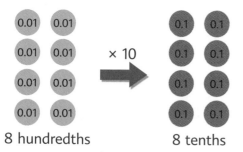

8 hundredths → 8 tenths

0.08 × 10 = 0.8

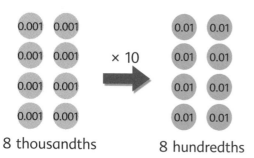

8 thousandths → 8 hundredths

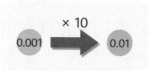

0.008 × 10 = 0.08

1. Multiply.
   (a) 0.6 × 10
   (b) 0.8 × 10
   (c) 0.9 × 10
   (d) 0.02 × 10
   (e) 0.04 × 10
   (f) 0.03 × 10
   (g) 0.005 × 10
   (h) 0.006 × 10
   (i) 0.007 × 10

2. Multiply 3.42 by 10.

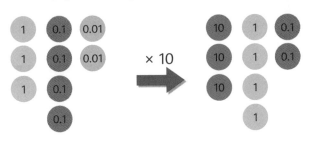

   3.42 × 10 = 34.2

3. Multiply 0.035 by 10.

Tens	Ones	•	Tenths	Hundredths	Thousandths
				3	5
			3	5	

   0.035 × 10 = 0.35
   $0.035 × 10^1 = 0.35$

   0.035

   When a decimal is **multiplied by 10**, we move the decimal point **one** place to the **right**.

4. Multiply.
   (a) 0.12 × 10
   (b) 0.068 × 10
   (c) 0.345 × 10
   (d) 2.05 × 10
   (e) 3.21 × 10
   (f) 1.439 × 10
   (g) 7.5 × 10
   (h) 10.4 × 10
   (i) 11.8 × 10

5. Multiply 0.53 by 40.

0.53 × 40 = 2.12 × 10

=

0.53 × 4 = 2.12

6. Multiply.

(a) 0.006 × 30   (b) 0.08 × 40   (c) 0.9 × 50

(d) 0.32 × 20   (e) 6.81 × 70   (f) 3.248 × 60

Exercise 9, page 17

7. Multiply 0.007 × 100.

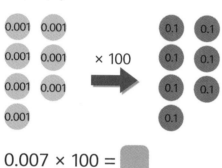

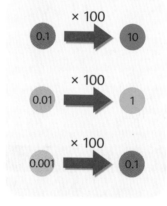

0.007 × 100 =

8. Multiply 4.23 by 100.

Hundreds	Tens	Ones	•	Tenths	Hundredths
		4		2	3
4	2	3			

4.23 × 100 = 423
4.23 × 10² = 423

$$4.23 \times 10^2 = 423$$

4.23

When a decimal is **multiplied by 100**, we move the decimal point **two** places to the **right**.

9. Multiply 0.006 by 1,000.

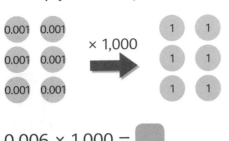

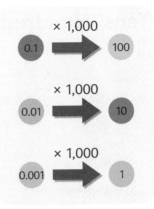

$0.006 \times 1,000 = \boxed{}$

10. Multiply 0.054 by 1,000.

Tens	Ones	•	Tenths	Hundredths	Thousandths
				5	4
5	4				

(× 1,000 arrows shown)

$0.054 \times 1,000 = 54$
$0.054 \times 10^3 = 54$

 0.054

When a decimal is **multiplied by 1,000**, we move the decimal point **three** places to the **right**.

11. Multiply.
   (a) 0.003×100 (b) 3.2×100 (c) 1.325×100
   (d) $0.09 \times 1,000$ (e) $3.62 \times 1,000$ (f) $13.4 \times 1,000$

12. Multiply 4.203 by 200.
   $4.203 \times 200 = 8.406 \times 100$

   $= \boxed{}$

   $4.203 \times 2 = 8.406$

13. Multiply 4.203 by 2,000.
   $4.203 \times 2,000 = 8.406 \times 1,000$

   $= \boxed{}$

14. Multiply.
   (a) 0.008×300 (b) 0.12×600 (c) 1.54×400
   (d) $0.03 \times 5,000$ (e) $0.25 \times 6,000$ (f) $5.12 \times 4,000$

Exercise 10, pages 18–19

6 Division by Tens, Hundreds, or Thousands

 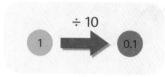 

3 ones   3 tenths

$$3 \div 10 = 0.3$$

3 tenths   3 hundredths

$$0.3 \div 10 = 0.03$$

3 hundredths   3 thousandths

$$0.03 \div 10 = 0.003$$

1. Divide.
   (a) $8 \div 10$
   (b) $0.8 \div 10$
   (c) $0.08 \div 10$
   (d) $2 \div 10$
   (e) $0.2 \div 10$
   (f) $0.02 \div 10$
   (g) $6 \div 10$
   (h) $0.6 \div 10$
   (i) $0.06 \div 10$

2. Divide 0.46 by 10.

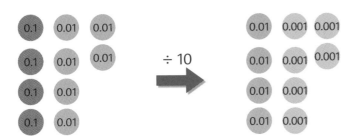

   $0.46 \div 10 = 0.046$

3. Divide 5.3 by 10.

Tens	Ones	•	Tenths	Hundredths	Thousandths
	5		3		
			5	3	

   $5.3 \div 10 = \dfrac{5.3}{10} = 0.53$

   $5.3 \div 10^1 = 5.3 \times \dfrac{1}{10^1} = 0.53$

   > When a decimal is **divided by 10**, we move
   > the decimal point **one** place to the **left**.

4. Divide.
   (a) $0.23 \div 10$
   (b) $0.45 \div 10$
   (c) $0.12 \div 10$
   (d) $2.5 \div 10$
   (e) $6.8 \div 10$
   (f) $5.3 \div 10$
   (g) $12 \div 10$
   (h) $39 \div 10$
   (i) $103 \div 10$

5. Divide 4.2 by 60.

   $4.2 \div 60 = 0.7 \div 10$

   $= \boxed{}$

    $4.2 \div 6 = 0.7$

6. Divide.

   (a) $8 \div 40$ (b) $16 \div 80$ (c) $63 \div 90$

   (d) $4.8 \div 60$ (e) $0.51 \div 30$ (f) $3.44 \div 80$

Exercise 11, page 20

7. Divide 4 by 100.

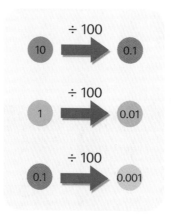

   $4 \div 100 = \boxed{}$

8. Divide 52.8 by 100.

Tens	Ones	•	Tenths	Hundredths	Thousandths
5	2		8		
			5	2	8

$52.8 \div 100 = \frac{52.8}{100} = 0.528$

$52.8 \div 10^2 = 52.8 \times \frac{1}{10^2} = 0.528$

 52.8

When a decimal is **divided by 100**, we move the decimal point **two** places to the **left**.

9. Divide 5 by 1,000.

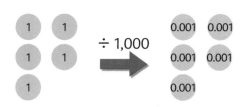

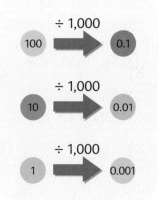

$5 \div 1,000 = \boxed{}$

10. Divide 62 by 1,000.

Tens	Ones	•	Tenths	Hundredths	Thousandths
6	2				
				6	2

$62 \div 1,000 = \dfrac{62}{1,000} = 0.062$

$62 \div 10^3 = 62 \times \dfrac{1}{10^3} = 0.062$

When a decimal is **divided by 1,000**, we move the decimal point **three** places to the **left**.

11. Divide.
   (a) $8 \div 100$
   (b) $90 \div 100$
   (c) $1.5 \div 100$
   (d) $4 \div 1,000$
   (e) $200 \div 1,000$
   (f) $324 \div 1,000$

12. Divide 46 by 200.
   $46 \div 200 = 23 \div 100 = \boxed{}$

   $46 \div 2 = 23$

13. Divide 46 by 2,000.
   $46 \div 2,000 = 23 \div 1,000 = \boxed{}$

14. Divide.
   (a) $0.8 \div 200$
   (b) $1.6 \div 400$
   (c) $4.8 \div 300$
   (d) $12 \div 6,000$
   (e) $65 \div 5,000$
   (f) $714 \div 7,000$

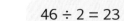
Exercise 12, pages 21–22

REVIEW 7

1. In 6.542, the digit '5' has the same value as _____.
   (A) 5 × 10   (B) $\frac{5}{10}$ (C) $\frac{5}{100}$ (D) 5 ÷ 1,000

2. $\frac{930}{1,000} + \frac{72}{100} + \frac{4}{10}$ expressed as a decimal is _____.
   (A) 1.006   (B) 2.05   (C) 10.06   (D) 20.5

3. The sum of 13 and 3.28 is _____.
   (A) 3.41   (B) 9.72   (C) 16.28   (D) 42.64

4. Two bags of salt have a mass of 5.4 kg. If one bag is two times as heavy as the other, what is the mass of the heavier bag?
   (A) 1.8 kg   (B) 2.7 kg   (C) 3.6 kg   (D) 8.1 kg

5. Select True or False.
   (a) 9.6 ÷ 100 = 0.96 ÷ 10   True / False
   (b) 2.032 = $2\frac{6}{125}$ True / False

6. Select True or False.
   (a) 3.94 is 3.945 rounded to 1 decimal place   True / False
   (b) 7 tenths less than 13.35 is 12.65   True / False

7. What is the value of the digit '5' in each of the following?
   (a) 10.275   (b) 58,026   (c) 36.254

8. What is the missing number in each 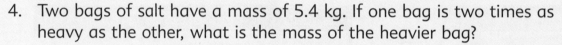?
   (a) 9.08 = 9 + ___
   (b) 8.602 = 8 + 0.6 + ___
   (c) 23.38 = 20 + 3 + ___ + 0.08
   (d) 1.909 = 1 + $\frac{\square}{10}$ + $\frac{9}{1,000}$

9. Write each of the following as a decimal.
   (a) 50 + 0.8 + 0.006
   (b) 7 + 3 × $\frac{1}{10^2}$ + 1 × $\frac{1}{10^3}$
   (c) 45 + $\frac{3}{10}$ + $\frac{8}{1,000}$
   (d) 8 + 9 × $\frac{1}{10^3}$
   (e) 0.009 + 0.4 + 9 + 60
   (f) 9 × $\frac{1}{10^3}$ + 7 + 8 × $\frac{1}{10}$ + 1 × $\frac{1}{10^2}$

10. Express each decimal as a fraction in its simplest form.

    (a) 0.6   (b) 4.40   (c) 6.105   (d) 7.225

    (e) 0.062   (f) 2.36   (g) 6.308   (h) 10.95

11. Express each fraction as a decimal.

    (a) $4\frac{7}{10}$ (b) $6\frac{9}{100}$ (c) $8\frac{21}{25}$ (d) $2\frac{9}{50}$

12. Divide. Give each answer as a decimal.

    (a) $42 \div 5$ (b) $23 \div 4$ (c) $15 \div 8$

13. Arrange each set of numbers in decreasing order.

    (a) $\frac{1}{6}$, 1.03, 1.09, $\frac{1}{16}$ (b) 3.022, 3.22, 3.202, 3.2

14. Arrange each set of numbers in increasing order.

    (a) 31,238, 31,832, 31,823, 31,328

    (b) $4\frac{1}{6}$, $\frac{9}{2}$, $4\frac{2}{5}$, $4\frac{3}{10}$

    (c) 4.98, 4.089, 498, 4,809

    (d) $2\frac{1}{2}$, 2.05, $2\frac{3}{5}$, 2.51

15. Round each number to the nearest whole number.

    (a) 8.9   (b) 8.07   (c) 0.899   (d) 109.5

16. (a) Round 3.592 to 1 decimal place.

    (b) Round 7.639 to 2 decimal places.

17. Express each fraction as a decimal correct to 1 decimal place.

    (a) $\frac{3}{4}$ (b) $\frac{4}{9}$ (c) $3\frac{1}{4}$ (d) $3\frac{5}{8}$

18. Express each fraction as a decimal correct to 2 decimal places.

    (a) $\frac{3}{7}$ (b) $\frac{2}{9}$ (c) $3\frac{5}{6}$

    (d) $\frac{4}{7}$ (e) $\frac{5}{6}$ (f) $3\frac{2}{9}$

19. Find the missing numbers.

    (a) $(20 \times 0.3) + (4 \times 0.3) = \boxed{} \times 0.3$

    (b) $(\frac{1}{2} \times 4) + (\frac{1}{2} \times 6) = \frac{1}{2} \times \boxed{}$

    (c) $(3 \times 7) + (0.4 \times 7) = \boxed{} \times 7$

    (d) $(400 \times 0.9) - (3 \times 0.9) = \boxed{} \times 0.9$

20. Multiply or divide.

    (a) 10×5.7 (b) 100×1.508 (c) $7.25 \times 1,000$

    (d) 36.8×10^3 (e) 0.034×10^2 (f) 1.2×10^6

    (g) $39 \div 10$ (h) $34.2 \div 100$ (i) $39 \div 1,000$

    (j) $30 \div 10^3$ (k) $9.3 \div 10^2$ (l) $40,000 \div 10^5$

21. Find the missing numbers.

    (a) $0.45 \times \boxed{} = 45$ (b) $\boxed{} \times 100 = 30.2$

    (c) $\boxed{} \div 10 = 210.8$ (d) $342 \div \boxed{} = 0.342$

22. Multiply 38 by 6. Then find the value of each of the following.

    (a) 0.038×6 (b) 0.038×600 (c) 3.8×60

23. Multiply 4.8 by 7. Then find the value of each of the following.

    (a) 4.8×70 (b) 4.8×700 (c) $0.48 \times 7,000$

24. Divide 56 by 8. Then find the value of each of the following.

    (a) $56 \div 80$ (b) $56 \div 800$ (c) $5.6 \div 80$

25. Divide 4.2 by 7. Then find the value of each of the following.

    (a) $4.2 \div 70$ (b) $4.2 \div 700$ (c) $0.42 \div 7$

26. Find the value of each of the following.

    (a) $3,000 \times 400$ (b) $6.04 \times 3,000$ (c) 3.25×6

    (d) $48,000 \div 2,000$ (e) $48.9 \div 100$ (f) $6.5 \div 2$

27. Estimate. Then find the actual value.

    (a) 4.32×6 (b) 9.128×5

    (c) $40.08 \div 3$ (d) $42.6 \div 8$

28. A rope is cut into pieces that are each 4.2 m long. If there are 20 pieces, how long was the rope?

29. Jane runs 10 times around the border of a field. If she runs a total distance of 5.2 miles, find the perimeter of the field in miles.

30. A farmer sold 200 chickens at $3.50 each. With the money he received from the sale, he bought 30 turkeys. Find the cost of 1 turkey correct to the nearest cent.

31. Mrs. Cohen bought 15 m of string. She used 2.5 m to tie a package. Then she cut the remainder into 6 equal pieces. Find the length of each piece. Give the answer in meters correct to 1 decimal place.

32. At a shop, 15 similar shirts cost $35. If 2 of them are sold at $4.90 each, and the rest are sold at $2.50 each, find the amount of money made.

33. Josh bought a motorcycle. He paid a deposit of $210 and 10 monthly installments of $31.25 each. Find the cost of the motorcycle.

34. Mrs. Garcia bought 2.5 kg of sugar. She used 325 g of it to make cookies and 1.45 kg to make cakes. How much sugar did she have left? Give the answer in kilograms.

35. Sean bought 10 apples and 8 pears. The apples cost $0.35 each. A pear cost twice as much as an apple. How much did he pay altogether?

36. Carlos has $2.50. Tom has twice as much as Carlos. Ryan has $5 more than Tom. How much do the three boys have altogether?

37. After cutting off a length of 6.32 m from a rope 20 m long, the remainder is divided into 8 equal pieces. What is the length of each piece? Give the answer in meters.

38. A microscope magnifies a bug 1,000 times when viewed through the microscope. If the bug is 0.00128 cm in length, how long will the bug appear when viewed through the microscope? Explain your answer.

8 MORE CALCULATIONS

1 Multiplication by a 2-Digit Whole Number

(a) Multiply 2,187 by 32.

Estimate :
2,187 × 32 ≈ 2,000 × 30
= 60,000

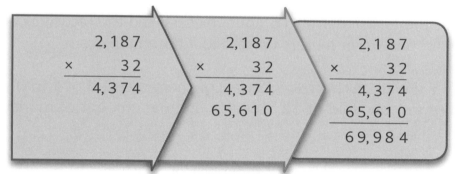

```
    2,187          2,187           2,187
  ×    32        ×    32         ×    32
    4,374          4,374           4,374
                  65,610          65,610
                                  69,984
```

The answer 69,984 is close to the estimate 60,000.
The answer is reasonable.

(b) Multiply 21.87 by 32.

Estimate:
21.87 × 32 ≈ 20 × 30
= 600

```
    21.87          21.87
  ×    32        ×    32
    43 74          43 74
  656 1          656 10
                 699.84
```

Remember to place the
decimal point correctly.

The answer 699.84 is close to the estimate 600.
The answer is reasonable.

How would you use (a)
to find (b) more quickly?

1. Estimate the value of each of the following.
   (a) 3,267 × 28
       3,267 × 28 ≈ 3,000 × 30 =

   (b) 326.7 × 28
       326.7 × 28 ≈ 300 × 30 =

   (c) 32.67 × 28
       32.67 × 28 ≈ 30 × 30 =

Exercise 1, page 29

2. (a) Estimate the value of 0.23 × 59.
       0.23 × 59 ≈ 0.2 × 60 = 12

   (b) Find the value of 0.23 × 59.

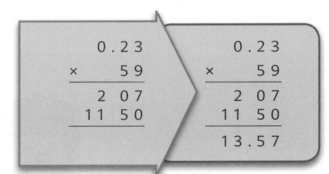

```
    0 . 2 3              0 . 2 3
  ×      5 9           ×      5 9
  ─────────            ─────────
    2  0 7              2  0 7
  1 1  5 0            1 1  5 0
  ─────────            ─────────
                      1 3 . 5 7
```

Remember to place the decimal point correctly.

3. Multiply.
   (a) 0.78 × 43   (b) 0.53 × 23   (c) 37 × 4.9
   (d) 23.7 × 26   (e) 40.6 × 45   (f) 18 × 132.4
   (g) 3.58 × 43   (h) 15.09 × 26   (i) 72 × 1.57

Exercise 2, pages 30–31

② Division by a 2-Digit Whole Number

(a) Divide 5,928 by 19.

Estimate:
$5,928 \div 19 \approx 6,000 \div 20$
$= 300$

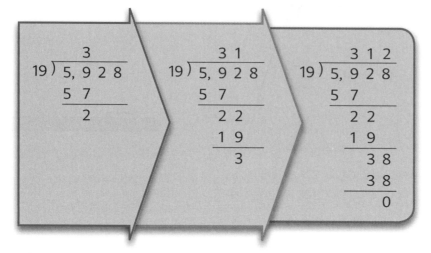

```
        3
   _____
19) 5, 9 2 8
    5 7
   _____
      2
```

```
        3 1
   _____
19) 5, 9 2 8
    5 7
   _____
      2 2
      1 9
   _____
        3
```

```
        3 1 2
   _____
19) 5, 9 2 8
    5 7
   _____
      2 2
      1 9
   _____
        3 8
        3 8
   _____
          0
```

The answer 312 is close to the estimate 300.
The answer is reasonable.

(b) Divide 59.28 by 19.

Estimate:
$59.28 \div 19 \approx 60 \div 20$
$= 3$

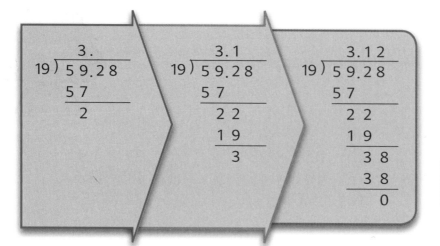

```
        3 .
   _____
19) 5 9 . 2 8
    5 7
   _____
      2
```

```
        3 . 1
   _____
19) 5 9 . 2 8
    5 7
   _____
      2 2
      1 9
   _____
        3
```

```
        3 . 1 2
   _____
19) 5 9 . 2 8
    5 7
   _____
      2 2
      1 9
   _____
        3 8
        3 8
   _____
          0
```

How would you use (a) to find (b) more quickly?

The answer 3.12 is close to the estimate 3.
The answer is reasonable.

1. Estimate the value of each of the following.

   (a) 2,877 ÷ 42

   2,877 ÷ 42 ≈ 2,800 ÷ 40 =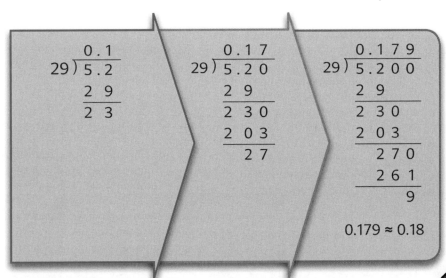

   (b) 287.7 ÷ 42

   287.7 ÷ 42 ≈ 280 ÷ 40 =

   (c) 28.77 ÷ 42

   28.77 ÷ 42 ≈ 28 ÷ 40 =

2. (a) Estimate the value of 5.2 ÷ 29.

   5.2 ÷ 29 ≈ 6 ÷ 30 = 0.2

   (b) Find the value of 5.2 ÷ 29 correct to 2 decimal places.

```
      0 . 1                    0 . 1 7                  0 . 1 7 9
  29) 5 . 2                29) 5 . 2 0              29) 5 . 2 0 0
      2 9                      2 9                      2 9
      -----                    -----                    -----
      2 3                      2 3 0                    2 3 0
                               2 0 3                    2 0 3
                               -----                    -----
                               2 7                      2 7 0
                                                        2 6 1
                                                        -----
                                                            9
```

0.179 ≈ 0.18

Estimate:
5.2 ÷ 29 ≈ 6 ÷ 30
        = 0.2

The answer 0.18 is close to the estimate 0.2. The answer is reasonable.

3. Find the value of each of the following correct to 2 decimal places.

   (a) 18 ÷ 16   (b) 0.49 ÷ 56   (c) 2.8 ÷ 23
   (d) 62.5 ÷ 31   (e) 15.9 ÷ 29   (f) 9.37 ÷ 32
   (g) 48.6 ÷ 21   (h) 10.28 ÷ 18   (i) 104.8 ÷ 42

Exercise 3, pages 32–33

③ Multiplication by a Decimal

$30 \times 0.1 = 30 \times \dfrac{1}{10}$

$\qquad\qquad = \dfrac{30}{10}$

$\qquad\qquad = 3$

$30 \times 0.01 = 30 \times \dfrac{1}{100}$

$\qquad\qquad\; = \dfrac{30}{100}$

$\qquad\qquad\; = \dfrac{3}{10}$

$\qquad\qquad\; = 0.3$

$3 \times 0.1 = 3 \times \dfrac{1}{10}$

$\qquad\quad = \dfrac{3}{10}$

$\qquad\quad = 0.3$

$3 \times 0.01 = 3 \times \dfrac{1}{100}$

$\qquad\qquad = \dfrac{3}{100}$

$\qquad\qquad = 0.03$

$0.3 \times 0.1 = \dfrac{3}{10} \times \dfrac{1}{10}$

$\qquad\qquad = \dfrac{3}{100}$

$\qquad\qquad = 0.03$

$0.3 \times 0.01 = \dfrac{3}{10} \times \dfrac{1}{100}$

$\qquad\qquad\; = \dfrac{3}{1000}$

$\qquad\qquad\; = 0.003$

1. Multiply 4.62 by 0.1.

Tens	Ones	•	Tenths	Hundredths	Thousandths
			4	6	2
		4	6	2	

×0.1 ×0.1 ×0.1

$4.62 \times 0.1 = 0.462$

> When a decimal is **multiplied by 0.1**, we move the decimal point **one** place to the **left**.

2. Multiply 16.3 by 0.01.

Tens	Ones	•	Tenths	Hundredths	Thousandths
1	6		3		
			1	6	3

×0.01 ×0.01 ×0.01

$16.3 \times 0.01 = 0.163$

> When a decimal is **multiplied by 0.01**, we move the decimal point **two** places to the **left**.

3. Multiply.
   (a) 0.6×0.1 (b) 0.06×0.1 (c) 5×0.1
   (d) 23×0.1 (e) 3.4×0.1 (f) 0.14×0.1
   (g) 4×0.01 (h) 0.4×0.01 (i) 8×0.01
   (j) 42×0.01 (k) 83.4×0.01 (l) 6.2×0.01

4. Study the following examples. What pattern do you see?

   $4 \times 2 = 8$
   $4 \times 0.2 = 4 \times 2 \times 0.1$
   $\quad\quad\quad = 8 \times 0.1$
   $\quad\quad\quad = 0.8$

   $4 \times 0.02 = 4 \times 2 \times 0.01$
   $\quad\quad\quad\; = 0.08$

   $0.4 \times 0.2 = 4 \times 0.1 \times 2 \times 0.1$
   $\quad\quad\quad\;\; = 4 \times 2 \times 0.1 \times 0.1$
   $\quad\quad\quad\;\; = 8 \times 0.02$
   $\quad\quad\quad\;\; = 0.08$

   $0.4 \times 0.02 = 4 \times 0.1 \times 2 \times 0.01$
   $\quad\quad\quad\quad\; = 4 \times 2 \times 0.01 \times 0.01$
   $\quad\quad\quad\quad\; = 8 \times 0.001$
   $\quad\quad\quad\quad\; = 0.008$

5. (a) Use 34 × 6 to solve 3.4 × 0.06.

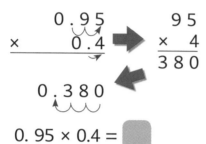

$$3.4 \times 0.06 = 34 \times 0.1 \times 6 \times 0.01$$
$$= 34 \times 6 \times 0.1 \times 0.01$$
$$= 204 \times 0.001$$
$$= 0.204$$

3. 4 × 0.06 = ☐

(b) Use 95 × 4 to solve 0.95 × 0.4.

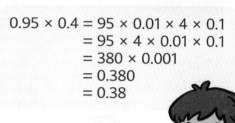

$$0.95 \times 0.4 = 95 \times 0.01 \times 4 \times 0.1$$
$$= 95 \times 4 \times 0.01 \times 0.1$$
$$= 380 \times 0.001$$
$$= 0.380$$
$$= 0.38$$

0. 95 × 0.4 = ☐

6. Multiply 2.35 by 0.8.

2.35 × 0.8 = ☐

$$
\begin{array}{r}
2.3\,5 \\
\times \quad 0.8 \\
\hline
\end{array}
\Rightarrow
\begin{array}{r}
2\,3\,5 \\
\times \quad 8 \\
\hline
1\,8\,8\,0 \\
\end{array}
$$

2.35 × 0.8 = 1.88

7. Estimate. Then multiply 22.8 by 0.7.

22.8 × 0.7 ≈ 20 × 0.7
= 14

20 × 7 = 140
20 × 0.7 = 14

22.8 × 0.7 = ☐

8. Multiply 11.8 by 0.05.

   $11.8 \times 0.05 = $ ▢

   $\begin{array}{r} 1\,1.8 \\ \times\quad 0.0\,5 \\ \hline \end{array}$ ➡ $\begin{array}{r} 1\,1\,8 \\ \times\qquad 5 \\ \hline 5\,9\,0 \end{array}$

   $11.8 \times 0.05 = 0.59$

9. Estimate. Then multiply 4.23 by 0.09.

   $4.2 \times 0.09 \approx 4 \times 0.09$
   $= 0.36$

   $4 \times 9 = 36$
   $4 \times 0.09 = 0.36$

   $4.2 \times 0.09 = $ ▢

10. Estimate. Then multiply.
    - (a) 0.3×0.6
    - (b) 4×0.7
    - (c) 0.23×0.5
    - (d) 3.9×0.7
    - (e) 48.2×0.4
    - (f) 9.42×0.3
    - (g) 0.4×0.06
    - (h) 5×0.07
    - (i) 2.9×0.05
    - (j) 3.9×0.04
    - (k) 48.2×0.02
    - (l) 12.7×0.03

     Exercise 4, pages 34–35

11. Estimate the value of each of the following.
    - (a) $3{,}957 \times 49$
      $3{,}957 \times 49 \approx 4{,}000 \times 50$
      $= $
    - (b) 395.7×49
      $395.7 \times 49 \approx 400 \times 50$
      $= $

    - (c) 395.7×4.9
      $395.7 \times 4.9 \approx 400 \times 5$
      $= $
    - (d) 395.7×0.49
      $395.7 \times 0.49 \approx 400 \times 0.5$
      $= $

    - (e) 39.57×4.9
      $39.57 \times 4.9 \approx 40 \times 5$
      $= $ ▢

    What patterns do you see?

12. (a) Estimate the value of 27.8 × 0.43.

27.8 × 0.43 ≈ 30 × 0.4

= ⬜

(b) Multiply 27.8 by 0.43.

```
  2 7.8            2 7 8
×  0.4 3         ×    4 3
                   8 3 4
                 1 1 1 2 0
                 1 1 9 5 4
```

27.8 × 0.43 = 27.8 × 43 × 0.01
            = 278 × 0.1 × 43 × 0.01
            = 278 × 43 × 0.1 × 0.01

27.8 × 0.43 = ⬜

13. (a) Estimate the value of 8.3 × 6.49.

8.3 × 6.49 ≈ 8 × 6

= ⬜

```
  6.4 9
× 8. 3
```

(b) Multiply 8.3 by 6.49.

8.3 × 6.49 ≈ ⬜

14. Multiply.
   (a) 7.4 × 4.3
   (b) 34.12 × 1.3
   (c) 9.4 × 28
   (d) 72 × 0.16
   (e) 8.3 × 0.21
   (f) 0.42 × 65
   (g) 84 × 0.13
   (h) 56 × 2.07
   (i) 1.29 × 29
   (j) 5.28 × 21
   (k) 0.45 × 45
   (l) 24 × 0.032
   (m) 0.398 × 41
   (n) 7.192 × 89
   (o) 49.97 × 38

Exercise 5, page 36

④ Division by a Decimal

$30 \div 0.1$ $= \dfrac{30}{0.1}$

$= \dfrac{30 \times 10}{0.1 \times 10}$

$= \dfrac{300}{1}$

$0.1\overline{)30}$ ➡ $1\overline{)300}$ (quotient 300)

$30 \div 0.01$ $= \dfrac{30}{0.01}$

$= \dfrac{30 \times 100}{0.01 \times 100}$

$= \dfrac{3,000}{1}$

$0.01\overline{)30}$ ➡ $1\overline{)3,000}$ (quotient $3,000$)

$30 \div 0.001 = \dfrac{30}{0.001}$

$= \dfrac{30 \times 1,000}{0.001 \times 1,000}$

$= \dfrac{30,000}{1}$

$0.001\overline{)30}$ ➡ $1\overline{)30,000}$ (quotient $30,000$)

$0.3 \div 0.1$ $= \dfrac{0.3}{0.1}$

$= \dfrac{0.3 \times 10}{0.1 \times 10}$

$= \dfrac{3}{1}$

$0.1\overline{)0.3}$ ➡ $1\overline{)3}$ (quotient 3)

$0.3 \div 0.01$ $= \dfrac{0.3}{0.01}$

$= \dfrac{0.3 \times 100}{0.01 \times 100}$

$= \dfrac{30}{1}$

$0.01\overline{)0.3}$ ➡ $1\overline{)30}$ (quotient 30)

$0.3 \div 0.001 = \dfrac{0.3}{0.001}$

$= \dfrac{0.3 \times 100}{0.001 \times 100}$

$= \dfrac{300}{1}$

$0.001\overline{)0.3}$ ➡ $1\overline{)300}$ (quotient 300)

1. Divide.
   (a) 500 ÷ 0.1
   (b) 500 ÷ 0.01
   (c) 500 ÷ 0.001
   (d) 50 ÷ 0.1
   (e) 50 ÷ 0.01
   (f) 50 ÷ 0.001
   (g) 5 ÷ 0.1
   (h) 5 ÷ 0.01
   (i) 5 ÷ 0.001
   (j) 0.5 ÷ 0.1
   (k) 0.5 ÷ 0.01
   (l) 0.5 ÷ 0.001
   (m) 0.05 ÷ 0.1
   (n) 0.05 ÷ 0.01
   (o) 0.05 ÷ 0.001
   (p) 0.005 ÷ 0.1
   (q) 0.005 ÷ 0.01
   (r) 0.005 ÷ 0.001

2. Find the value of each of the following.
   (a) 6 ÷ 3

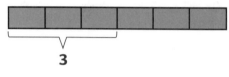

   3

   $6 \div 3 = \boxed{}$

   How many 3's are there in 6?

   (b) 6 ÷ 0.3

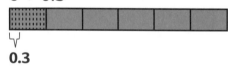

   0.3

   $6 \div 0.3 = \boxed{}$

   How many 0.3's are there in 6?
   0.3 = 3 tenths.
   There are 60 tenths in 6.

   $6 \div 0.3 = \dfrac{6}{0.3} = \dfrac{6 \times 10}{0.3 \times 10} = \dfrac{60}{3} = 20$

   There are 20 groups of 3 tenths in 6.

3. (a) Estimate the value of 5.94 ÷ 0.7.

   $5.94 \div 0.7 = \dfrac{5.94}{0.7}$

   $= \dfrac{5.94 \times 10}{0.7 \times 10}$

   $= \dfrac{59.4}{7}$

   $= \dfrac{\boxed{}}{7}$

   $= \boxed{}$

   I can make a quick estimate this way:
   59.4 is between 56 and 63.
   The answer will be between 8 and 9.

(b) Find the value of 5.94 ÷ 0.7 correct to 2 decimal places.

$0.7\overline{)5.94}$ ⟶ $7\overline{)59.4}$

Move the decimal point of both numbers the same amount to the right so that the number we are dividing by is a whole number.

$0.7\overline{)5.94}$ ➡ $7\overline{)59.4}$ ➡

$$
\begin{array}{r}
8.4 \\
7\overline{)59.4} \\
56 \\
\hline
34 \\
28 \\
\hline
6
\end{array}
$$
➡
$$
\begin{array}{r}
8.485... \\
7\overline{)59.400} \\
56 \\
\hline
34 \\
28 \\
\hline
60 \\
56 \\
\hline
40 \\
35 \\
\hline
5 \\
\vdots
\end{array}
$$

5.94 ÷ 0.7 ≈ ⬚

OR

5.94 ÷ 0.7 = 8.49 (correct to 2 decimal places)

4. Estimate the value of each of the following.

(a) 4,598 ÷ 3
4,598 ÷ 3 ≈ 4,500 ÷ 3
= ⬚

(b) 4,598 ÷ 0.3
4,598 ÷ 0.3 ≈ 4,500 ÷ 0.3
= 45,000 ÷ 3
= ⬚

(c) 45.98 ÷ 0.3
45.98 ÷ 0.3 ≈ 45.00 ÷ 0.3
= 450 ÷ 3
= ⬚

(d) 4.598 ÷ 0.03
4.598 ÷ 0.03 ≈ 4.500 ÷ 0.03
= 450 ÷ 3
= ⬚

5. Find the value of each of following correct to at most 2 decimal places.

(a) 45.9 ÷ 0.3

(b) 89.98 ÷ 0.04

(c) 100 ÷ 0.008

Exercise 6, pages 37—38

6. Estimate the value of each of the following.
   (a) $3,687 \div 42$
       $3,687 \div 42 \approx 3,600 \div 40$
       $= \boxed{}$

   (b) $3,687 \div 4.2$
       $3,687 \div 4.2 \approx 3,600 \div 4$
       $= \boxed{}$

   (c) $3,687 \div 0.42$
       $3,687 \div 0.42 \approx 3,600 \div 0.4$
       $= 36,000 \div 4$
       $= \boxed{}$

   (d) $36.87 \div 4.2$
       $36.87 \div 4.2 \approx 36 \div 4$
       $= \boxed{}$

   (e) $36.87 \div 0.042$
       $36.87 \div 0.042 \approx 36 \div 0.04$
       $= 3,600 \div 4$
       $= \boxed{}$

7. (a) Estimate the value of $128.7 \div 0.24$.
       $128.7 \div 0.24 \approx 120 \div 0.2$
       $= 1,200 \div 2 = \boxed{}$

   (b) Find the value of $128.7 \div 0.24$ correct to 2 decimal places.

$$0.24\,\overline{)128.7} \quad \Rightarrow \quad 24\,\overline{)12870}$$

$$\begin{array}{r} 536 \\ 24\,\overline{)12870} \\ 120 \\ \hline 87 \\ 72 \\ \hline 150 \\ 144 \\ \hline 6 \end{array}$$

$$\begin{array}{r} 536.25 \\ 24\,\overline{)12870.00} \\ 120 \\ \hline 87 \\ 72 \\ \hline 150 \\ 144 \\ \hline 60 \\ 48 \\ \hline 120 \\ 120 \\ \hline 0 \end{array}$$

$128.7 \div 0.24 = \boxed{}$

8. Find the value of each of following correct to at most 2 decimal places.
   (a) $45.9 \div 1.8$
   (b) $42.98 \div 0.16$
   (c) $15 \div 0.006$
   (d) $1 \div 2.5$
   (e) $3.6 \div 24$
   (f) $15.2 \div 1.2$
   (g) $96.8 \div 4.7$
   (h) $256.8 \div 0.24$
   (i) $14.56 \div 0.91$

52

Exercise 7, page 39

5 Conversion of Measures

The table shows the heights of 3 boys in meters.
Express the heights in centimeters.

Name	Height
Sam	1.4 m
Ryan	1.26 m
Matthew	1.32 m

1 m = 100 cm

0.1 m = 10 cm

0.01 m = 1 cm

0.4 m = 0.4 × 100 cm
     = 40 cm

1.4 m = 100 cm + 40 cm
     = 140 cm

Sam's height is 140 cm.

Ryan's height is ⬚ cm.

Matthew's height is ⬚ cm.

Use a tape measure to find a friend's height in meters and centimeters.
What is the height in meters only?

1. (a) Express 0.75 m in centimeters.
   0.75 m = 0.75 × 100 cm

   = [ ] cm

   (b) Express 3.75 m in centimeters.
   3.75 m = 3.75 × 100 cm

   = [ ] cm

   (c) Express 2.8 kg in grams.
   2.8 kg = 2.8 × 1,000 g

   = [ ] g

1 m = 100 cm
1 km = 1,000 m
1 yd = 3 ft
1 ft = 12 in.
1 kg = 1,000 g
1 lb = 16 oz
1 L = 1,000 ml
1 gal = 4 qt
1 qt = 2 pt
1 qt = 4 c

2. (a) Express 0.5 ft in inches.
   0.5 ft = 0.5 × 12 in.

   = [ ] in.

I know that 0.5 is $\frac{1}{2}$.
I find $\frac{1}{2}$ of 12.

   (b) Express 6.25 lb in ounces.
   6.25 lb = 6.25 × 16 oz

   = [ ] oz

It is easy to find 0.25
of 16. It is the same as
$\frac{1}{4}$ of 16.

3. Find the equivalent measures.

   (a) 0.6 m = [ ] cm   (b) 0.49 L = [ ] ml

   (c) 0.615 km = [ ] m   (d) 0.3 kg = [ ] g

   (e) 1.85 kg = [ ] g   (f) 4.2 L = [ ] ml

   (g) 2.75 qt = [ ] c   (h) 3.5 lb = [ ] oz

   (i) 3.25 ft = [ ] in.   (j) 0.5 gal = [ ] qt

4. (a) Express 4.2 L in liters and milliliters.

4.2 L = 4 L ml   0.2 L = 0.2 × 1,000 ml

(b) Express 8.75 ft in feet and inches.

8.75 ft = 8 ft in. $0.75 = \frac{3}{4}$

$\frac{3}{4}$ of 12 =

(c) Express 5.3 lb in pounds and ounces to the nearest ounce.

5.3 lb ≈ 5 lb ☐ oz

I will use decimals instead of fractions.

0.3 × 16 =

5. Find the equivalent measures.

(a) 3.45 km = ☐ km ☐ m   (b) 2.06 m = ☐ m ☐ cm

(c) 4.005 L = ☐ L ☐ ml   (d) 6.432 kg = ☐ kg ☐ g

(e) 4.25 lb = ☐ lb ☐ oz   (f) 7.5 ft = ☐ ft ☐ in.

Exercise 8, page 40

6. Express 145 ml in liters.

$145 \text{ ml} = \frac{145}{1,000} \text{ L}$

= ☐ L

145.0

7. Express 9 inches in feet.

$9 \text{ in.} = \frac{9}{12} \text{ ft}$

= ☐ ft

8. Find the equivalent measures.

(a) 350 m = ☐ km

(b) 420 ml = ☐ L

(c) 625 g = ☐ kg

(d) 30 cm = ☐ m

(e) 84 oz = ☐ lb

(f) 42 min = ☐ hr

9. Express 3 kg 500 g in kilograms.
   3 kg 500 g = 3 kg + 0.5 kg

   = ☐ kg

500 g = 0.5 kg

10. Find the equivalent measures.

(a) 4 m 35 cm = ☐ m

(b) 5 km 90 m = ☐ km

(c) 2 L 800 ml = ☐ L

(d) 4 kg 75 g = ☐ kg

(e) 3 ft 9 in. = ☐ ft

(f) 3 qt 2 c = ☐ qt

11. Express 3,080 g in kilograms.

Method 1:

3,080 g = 3 kg 80 g

= ☐ kg

Method 2:

$3,080 \text{ g} = \frac{3,080}{1,000} \text{ kg}$

= ☐ kg

3,080.0

12. Find the equivalent measures.

(a) 4,070 m = ☐ km

(b) 2,380 ml = ☐ L

(c) 5,200 g = ☐ kg

(d) 605 cm = ☐ m

(e) 51 in. = ☐ ft

(f) 88 oz = ☐ lb

Exercise 9, pages 41—42

REVIEW 8

1. If $0.01 \times$ _____ $= 0.034$, what is the missing number?
   (A) 0.034　　(B) 0.34　　(C) 3.4　　(D) 34

2. $\dfrac{78}{0.6}$ is the same as _____.
   (A) $7.8 \div 6$　　(B) $78 \div 6$　　(C) $780 \div 6$　　(D) $780 \div 60$

3. 7 kg 30 g is the same as _____.
   (A) 7.003 kg　(B) 7.03 kg　　(C) 7.3 kg　　(D) 7.30 kg

4. How many 1.2 L bottles can be completely filled from two bottles of water, one containing 8.75 L and the other 4.45 L?
   (A) 10　　　　(B) 11　　　　(C) 12　　　　(D) 13

5. Select True or False.
   (a) $4.3 \times 0.4 = (4 \times 0.4) + (0.4 \times 0.3)$　　　　True / False
   (b) The whole number nearest to 3.2×7.8 is 24.　　　True / False

6. Select True or False.
   (a) 45 ounces = 3.75 pounds　　　　True / False
   (b) 235.2 inches = 19.6 feet　　　　True / False

7. Estimate the value of each of the following.
   (a) $6.254 \div 72$
   (b) $33.14 \div 58$
   (c) $375.23 \div 69$

8. (a) Find the product of 4.2 and 1.19.
   (b) Find the quotient of 4.59 divided by 0.6.

9. What is the missing number in each ▢ ?

   (a) $1 = \boxed{} \times 10$

   (b) $0.1 \times \boxed{} = 100$

   (c) $0.1 \times \boxed{} = 0.001$

   (d) $0.01 \div \boxed{} = 100$

   (e) $10 = \boxed{} \div 0.01$

   (f) $0.1 \div \boxed{} = 1,000$

   (g) $\boxed{} \times 0.5 = 150$

   (h) $\boxed{} \times 0.08 = 9.6$

   (i) $\boxed{} \div 0.9 = 117$

   (j) $0.4 \div \boxed{} = 0.05$

10. Multiply.

    (a) 3.43×40 (b) 4.06×78 (c) 21.5×0.45

11. Find the value of each of the following.

    (a) 34×0.4 (b) 4.5×6.2
    (c) 1.26×0.31 (d) $3.7 \div 0.2$
    (e) $45.6 \div 12$ (f) $0.657 \div 0.18$

12. Find the value of each of the following.
    Then round to the nearest whole number.

    (a) 2.56×32 (b) 45.62×0.6 (c) $56.32 \div 3.2$

13. Estimate the value of each of the following.
    Then give the answers correct to 1 decimal place.

    (a) 9.45×0.5 (b) 0.34×5.02
    (c) 80.4×1.6 (d) $4.59 \div 0.3$
    (e) $0.43 \div 0.21$ (f) $38 \div 0.012$

14. Find the missing numbers.

    (a) $0.9 \times \boxed{} = 0.072$

    (b) $\boxed{} \div 6.2 = 43.1$

    (c) $\boxed{} \times 0.71 = 4.402$

    (d) $3.45 \div \boxed{} = 15$

15. Find the equivalent measures.

(a) 0.258 L = ☐ ml

(b) 0.75 gal = ☐ qt

(c) 0.085 km = ☐ m

(d) 0.25 ft = ☐ in.

(e) 0.706 kg = ☐ g

(f) 0.5 lb = ☐ oz

16. Find the equivalent measures.

(a) 670 ml = ☐ L

(b) 12 oz = ☐ lb

(c) 105 m = ☐ km

(d) 3 c = ☐ qt

(e) 69 g = ☐ kg

(f) 6 in. = ☐ ft

17. Find the equivalent measures.

(a) 20.08 km = ☐ km ☐ m

(b) 3.75 qt = ☐ qt ☐ c

(c) 16.5 L = ☐ L ☐ ml

(d) 18.5 ft = ☐ ft ☐ in.

(e) 2.08 kg = ☐ kg ☐ g

(f) 4.75 lb = ☐ lb ☐ oz

18. Find the equivalent measures.

(a) 9 m 60 cm = ☐ m

(b) 6 gal 3 qt = ☐ qt

(c) 4 L 705 ml = ☐ L

(d) 2 lb 5 oz = ☐ oz

(e) 25 km 6 m = ☐ km

(f) 3 ft 7 in. = ☐ in.

19. Copy and write >, <, or = in each ◯.

(a) 950 ml ◯ 1 L

(b) 2.038 km ◯ 38 m

(c) 0.09 m ◯ 9 cm

(d) 3.5 L ◯ 3 L 5 ml

(e) 1.25 kg ◯ 1 kg 25 g

(f) 10.08 kg ◯ 10 kg 80 g

(g) 82 in. ◯ 7 ft

(h) 6.5 lb ◯ 104 oz

20. The area of a parallelogram is 53.3 cm². If the height is 6.5 cm, what is the length of the base?

21. Jamie has $31.75 in quarters. How many quarters does he have?

22. A pole is 16.2 m long. Susan cut 5.7 m from it and divided the remainder into 7 equal pieces. How long is each piece?

23. Kyle saves $0.60 and Yvonne saves $0.80 each day. Yvonne has saved $5.60 more than Kyle. How much has Kyle saved now?

24. The price of an apple is one third that of an orange. Robert paid $10.80 for 5 oranges and 12 apples.
    (a) How many apples could he buy for $10.80?
    (b) How much does one apple cost?

25. A red rope is 0.2 times longer than a blue rope. Both ropes are cut into pieces, each of length 0.15 m. The blue rope is cut into 268 pieces with a remainder of 0.05 m long.
    (a) How long is the red rope?
    (b) How many more pieces of red rope than blue rope are there?

26. David multiplied 3.47 by 0.9 and got the answer 31.23.
    Is his answer correct? Why?

Review 8, pages 43–45

9 VOLUME

① Cubic Units

Draw a cube.

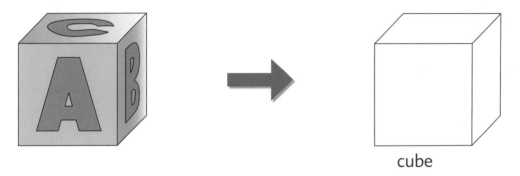

cube

All the edges of a cube are of equal length.
The sides are all squares.

Draw a cuboid.

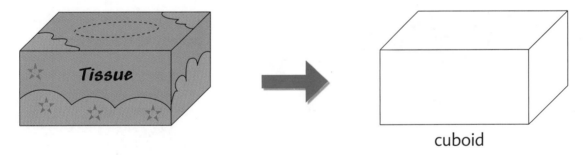

cuboid

How is a cuboid different from a cube?
What are the shapes of all the sides?

Cubes and cuboids are called **rectangular prisms**.
Rectangular prisms are **solid figures**.

We can draw a cube or a cuboid in other ways.

 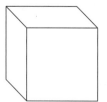

 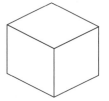

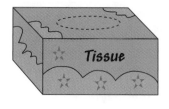 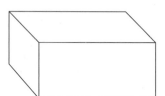

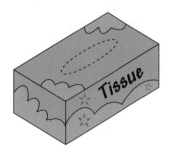 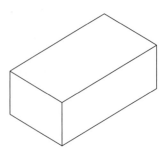

1.

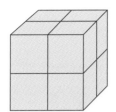

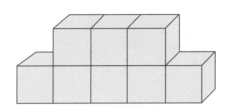

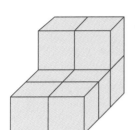

We measure volume in cubic units.
These solids have the same volume.

The volume of each solid is 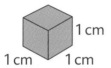 cubic units.

The volume of a unit cube
() is 1 **cubic unit**.

2. (a) Each edge of the cube is 1 cm long.

1 cm
1 cm   1 cm

The cubic centimeter (cm³) is a unit of volume.

The volume of the cube is cubic centimeter (cm³).

(b) Each edge of the cube is 1 in. long.

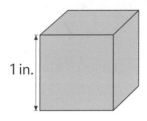

1 in.

We can also use other cubic measures, such as the cubic inch (in.³), cubic foot (ft³), or cubic meter (m³).

The volume of the cube is cubic inch (in.³).

3. The following solids are made up of 1-cm cubes.
   Find the volume of each solid.

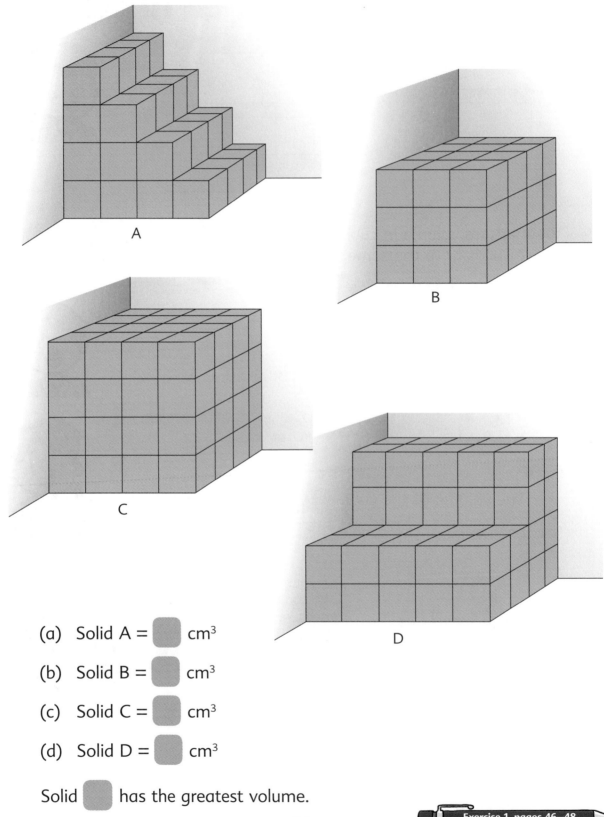

(a) Solid A = ☐ cm³

(b) Solid B = ☐ cm³

(c) Solid C = ☐ cm³

(d) Solid D = ☐ cm³

Solid ☐ has the greatest volume.

Exercise 1, pages 46–48

❷ Volume of Rectangular Prisms

The rectangular prism is made up of 1-cm cubes.

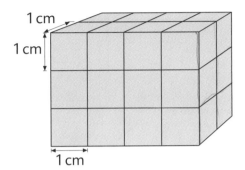

$4 \times 2 = 8$
There are 8 cubes in each layer.

$8 \times 3 = 24$
There are 24 cubes altogether.

The length of the rectangular prism is 4 cm.
Its width is 2 cm.
Its height is 3 cm.

$4 \times 2 \times 3$

Its volume is cm³.

The rectangular prism measures 4 cm by 2 cm by 3 cm.

Volume of rectangular prism = length × width × height

$$V = l \times w \times h$$

We turn the rectangular prism so that it rests on a different side as shown on the right.

What is the new length, width and height? Has the volume changed?

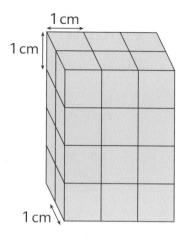

1 cm
1 cm
1 cm

1. Find the volume of the rectangular prism which measures 5 cm by 2 cm by 3 cm.

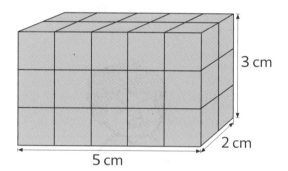

3 cm
2 cm
5 cm

$V = l \times w \times h$

Volume of the rectangular prism = 5 × 2 × 3

= ⬜ cm³

2. Find the volume of each rectangular prism.

(a)

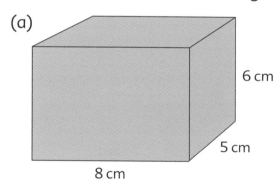

6 cm
5 cm
8 cm

(b)

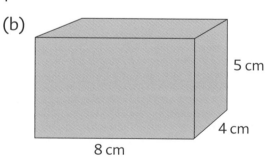

5 cm
4 cm
8 cm

66

3. Find the volume of each cube.

(a)

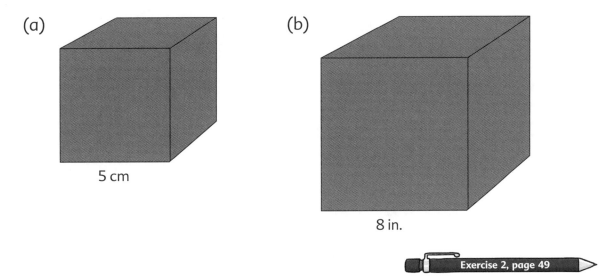

5 cm

(b)

8 in.

Exercise 2, page 49

4. The plastic box measures 10 cm by 10 cm by 10 cm.
   It can hold 1 L of water.

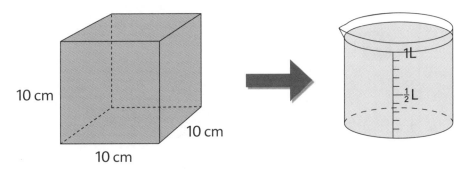

10 cm

10 cm

10 cm

Maximum volume of water that
the box can contain = 10 × 10 × 10

= ⬜ cm³

1 L = ⬜ cm³

1 ml = ⬜ cm³

1 L = 1,000 ml

5. (a) Express 2.5 L in cubic centimeters.

 2.5 L = 2.5 × 1,000 cm³

 = ⬜ cm³

1 L = 1,000 cm³

(b) Express 3,200 cm³ in liters.

 3,200 cm³ = $\frac{3,200}{1,000}$ L

 = ⬜ L

6. A rectangular tank measures 40 cm by 25 cm by 30 cm. How many liters of water are in the tank when it is full? (1 L = 1,000 cm³)

Volume of water = 40 × 25 × 30

 = ⬜ cm³

 = ⬜ L

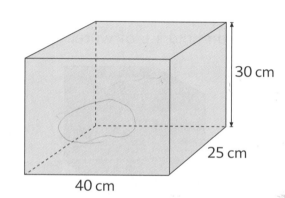

30 cm

25 cm

40 cm

7. A rectangular container, 12 cm long and 10 cm wide, is filled with water to a depth of 5 cm. Find the volume of water in the container.

Volume of water = 12 × 10 × 5

 = ⬜ cm³

 = ⬜ L

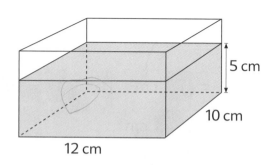

5 cm

10 cm

12 cm

Exercise 3, page 50

68

8. The following solid is made from centimeter cubes.
   Find the volume.

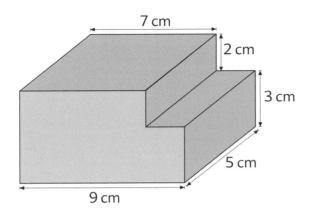

Method 1:

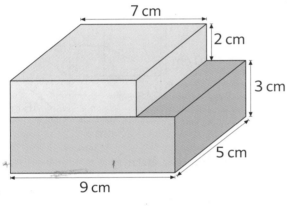

Volume = (7 × 5 × 2) + (9 × 5 × 3)

$= \boxed{} + \boxed{}$

$= \boxed{}$ cm³

Method 2:

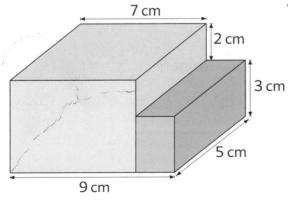

Volume = (7 × 5 × 5) + (2 × 5 × 3)

$= \boxed{} + \boxed{}$

$= \boxed{}$ cm³

Method 3:

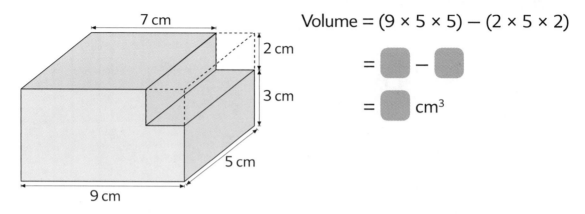

Volume $= (9 \times 5 \times 5) - (2 \times 5 \times 2)$

$$= \boxed{} - \boxed{}$$

$$= \boxed{} \text{ cm}^3$$

9. A rectangular tank measuring 25 cm by 16 cm by 30 cm is filled with water to a depth of 12 cm.

   (a) Find the volume of water in the tank.

   Volume of water $= 25 \times 12 \times 16$

   $$= \boxed{} \text{ cm}^3$$

   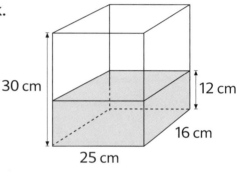

   (b) How much more water is needed to fill the tank?

   Increase in height of water level $= 30 - 12$
   $$= 18 \text{ cm}$$

   Volume of water needed $= 25 \times 16 \times 18$

   $$= \boxed{} \text{ cm}^3$$

   (c) What is the total capacity of the container?

   Capacity of the container $= \boxed{} \text{ cm}^3$

10. This container is filled with water to a depth of 30 cm.

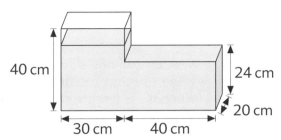

40 cm   24 cm   20 cm
30 cm   40 cm

(a) Find the volume of the water in the container.

Volume of water in A = ☐ cm³

Volume of water in B = ☐ cm³

Total volume of water = ☐ cm³

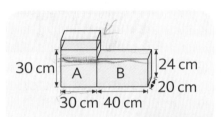

30 cm   A   B   24 cm   20 cm
30 cm 40 cm

(b) Find another way to calculate the volume.

11. The following solid is made up from 2-cm cubes.
    What is it's volume?

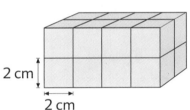

2 cm
2 cm

Method 1:

I find the length
of each side first.

Length = ☐ cm

Width = ☐ cm

Height = ☐ cm

Volume = ☐ cm³

Method 2:

I find the volume
of 1 cube first.

Volume of
1 cube = ☐ cm³

Volume of
16 cubes = ☐ cm³

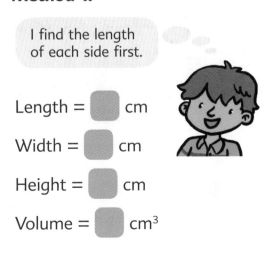

Exercise 4, pages 51–53

12. (a) One face of the rectangular prism has an area of 10 cm².
    The height of the rectangular prism is 3 cm.
    Find its volume.

Top surface area = 10 cm²

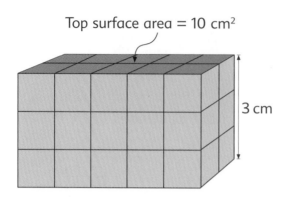

3 cm

We can call one side the base.
If we say that the area of
the base is length × width,
then we can say that the
volume = base × height.
$V = b \times h$.

Volume of rectangular prism = 10 × 3

= ⬚ cm³

(b) Find the volume of the prism using a different base.

Area = ⬚ cm²

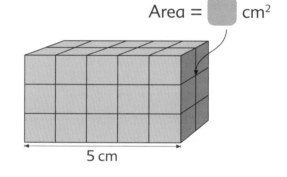

5 cm

Volume = ⬚ × 5

= ⬚ cm³

Volume = ⬚ × 2

= ⬚ cm³

2 cm

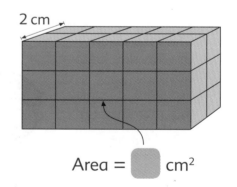

Area = ⬚ cm²

13. Find the volume of each rectangular prism.

(a)

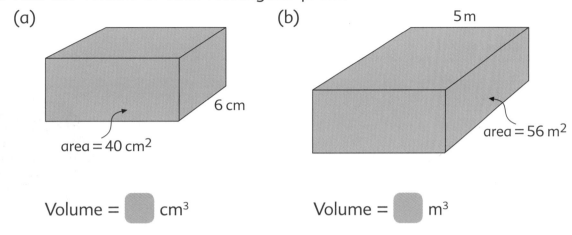

6 cm

area = 40 cm²

Volume = ▢ cm³

(b)

5 m

area = 56 m²

Volume = ▢ m³

14. A rectangular tank has a base area of 6 m².
It contains water to a depth of 2 m.
Find the volume of water in the tank.

Volume of water = 6 × 2

= ▢ m³

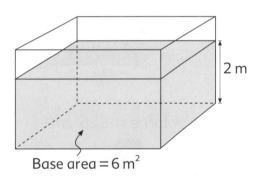

2 m

Base area = 6 m²

Exercise 5, page 54

15. The volume of a cube is 27 cm³.
Find the length of one edge of the cube.

▢ × ▢ × ▢ = 27

The length of each edge of the cube is ▢ cm.

16. The volume of a rectangular prism is 24 cm³. The length of the rectangular prism is 3 cm and its width is 2 cm. Find its height.

$V = l \times w \times h$

$h = V \div (l \times w)$

$\quad = \dfrac{V}{l \times w}$

$\quad = \dfrac{24}{3 \times 2}$

$\quad = \boxed{}\ \text{cm}^3$

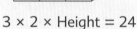
3 × 2 × Height = 24

17. Find the unknown edge of each rectangular prism.

(a)

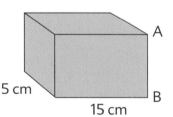

5 cm
15 cm
A
B

Volume = 525 cm³

AB = ▢ cm

(b)

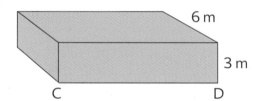

6 m
3 m
C
D

Volume = 216 m³

CD = ▢ m

18. Find the unknown edge of each rectangular prism.

(a)

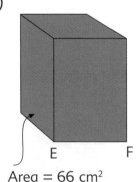

E   F
Area = 66 cm²

Volume = 264 cm³

EF = ▢ cm

(b)

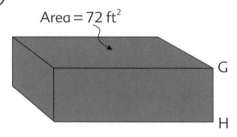

Area = 72 ft²
G
H

Volume = 288 ft³

GH = ▢ ft

19. A rectangular container, 8 cm long and 5 cm wide, contains 120 cm³ of water. Find the height of the water level in the container.

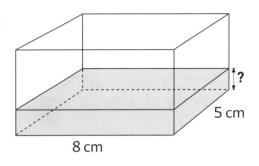

Height of water level = $\dfrac{120}{8 \times 5}$

= ◻ cm

20. A rectangular container, 20 cm long and 10 cm wide, contains 2.5 L of water. Find the height of the water level in the container.
(1 L = 1,000 cm³)

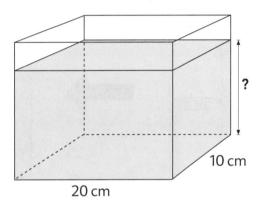

Volume of water = 2.5 L
= 2.5 × 1,000 cm³
= 2,500 cm³

Height of water level = $\dfrac{2,500}{20 \times 10}$

= ◻ cm

21. A rectangular container measuring 20 cm by 10 cm by 10 cm is filled with water to its brim. If 0.75 L of water is poured out from the container, what will be the height of the water level left in the container?

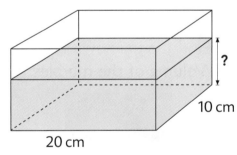

Decrease in height of water level = $\dfrac{750}{20 \times 10}$

= ◻ cm

Height of remaining water level = 10 − ◻

= ◻ cm

75

Exercise 6, pages 55–58

③ Finding the Volume of a Solid

Diego poured 50 ml of water into a measuring cylinder.
Then he put in some marbles and measured the
volume of water displaced by the marbles.

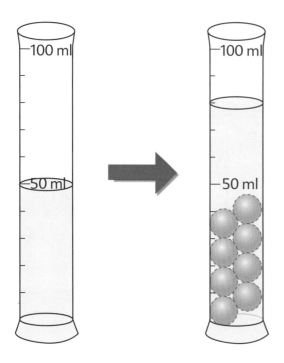

$1 \text{ ml} = 1 \text{ cm}^3$

Volume of water = 50 cm³

Volume of water and the marbles = ▢ cm³

Volume of the marbles = ▢ cm³

Volume of marbles = volume of water displaced

1. A rectangular tank, 30 cm long and 20 cm wide, is filled with water to a depth of 8 cm. When a stone was put in, the water level rose to 11 cm. Find the volume of the stone.
   (Assume that the stone is completely under water).

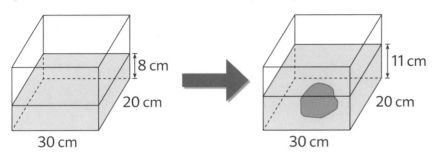

Increase in height of water level = 11 − 8
                                  = 3 cm

Volume of water displaced = 30 × 20 × 3
                          = ⬜ cm³

Volume of stone = ⬜ cm³

The water level rose by 3 cm.

2. A rectangular tank, 30 cm long and 18 cm wide, contained some water and a stone. When the stone was taken out, the water level dropped by 2 cm. Find the volume of the stone.
   (Assume that the stone was completely under water.)

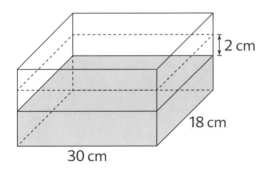

Decrease in height of water level = 2 cm

Volume of stone = 30 × 18 × 2
                = ⬜ cm³

3. A rectangular container, 15 cm long and 10 cm wide, contains water to a depth of 4 cm. When a stone of volume 300 cm³ is put in, the water level rises. Find the height of the new water level.
   (Assume that the stone is completely under water).

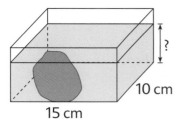

15 cm

10 cm

?

Increase in height $= \dfrac{300}{15 \times 10}$

$= \boxed{}$ cm

New height $= \boxed{}$ cm

The height of the new water level is $\boxed{}$ cm.

4. A rectangular container, 9 cm long and 6 cm wide, was filled with water to a depth of 5 cm. When some marbles were added into the container, the depth of the water became 7 cm. Find the total volume of the marbles.

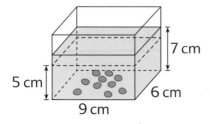

7 cm

5 cm

6 cm

9 cm

Change in depth of water $= \boxed{}$ cm

Change in volume $= \boxed{}$ cm³

The total volume of the marbles is $\boxed{}$ cm³.

5. Three identical cubes of edge 20 cm are placed in an empty rectangular tank. 136 L of water are then used to fill the tank. The width and height of the tank are 80 cm each. What is the length of the tank?

Exercise 7, pages 59–60

1. The figure shows a solid made up of 2-cm cubes. What is the volume of the solid?

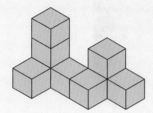

   (A) 7 cm³   (B) 9 cm³   (C) 56 cm³   (D) 72 cm³

2. A tank has a height of 3 m and a base of 2 m². It is $\frac{1}{3}$-filled with water. How much water is in the tank?

   (A) 2m³   (B) 4m³   (C) 8 m³   (D) 12m³

3. What is 1,050 cm³ in liters and milliliters?

   (A) 1 L 50 ml   (B) 1 L 500 ml
   (C) 10 L 50 ml   (D) 10 L 500 ml

4. The volume of a rectangular solid is 960 cm³. It is 12 cm wide and 5 cm high. What is its length?

   (A) 16 cm   (B) 80 cm   (C) 192 cm   (D) 400 cm

5. Select True or False.
   (a) The volume of a cube of side 6 cm is 36 cm².   True / False
   (b) The volume of a box is 120 cm³. It has a length
       of 6 cm and a width of 4 cm. Its height is less
       than its width.   True / False

6. Select True or False.
   (a) A rectangular tank measures 1.5 m by 300 cm by
       2.1 m. It is one-third-filled with water. The volume
       of the water in the tank is $\frac{1}{3}$ × 1.5 × 300 × 2.1 m³.   True / False
   (b) The solid on the right has a
       volume of 324 cm³. The volume
       of one cube is 12 cm³.

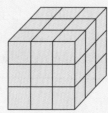

                                                             True / False

7. Find the volume of each rectangular prism.

(a)

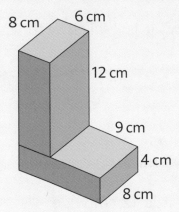

10 in. 3 in. 4 in.

(b)

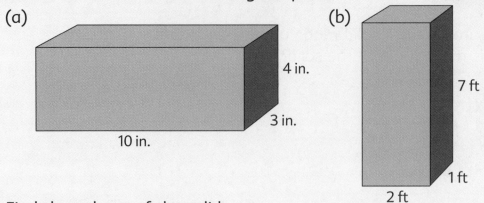

7 ft 1 ft 2 ft

8. Find the volume of the solid.

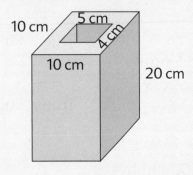

8 cm 6 cm 12 cm 9 cm 4 cm 8 cm

9. A wooden block has a rectangular hole through its center. Find the volume of the block.

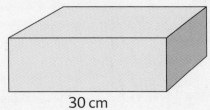

10 cm 5 cm 4 cm 10 cm 20 cm

10. The area of the shaded face of the rectangular prism is 400 cm². Find the volume of the rectangular prism.

30 cm

11. A tank is $\frac{3}{5}$-filled with water. When 500 ml of water is poured out, the tank becomes $\frac{1}{2}$ full. Find the capacity of the tank in liters.

12. Find the unknown edge of each rectangular prism.

(a)

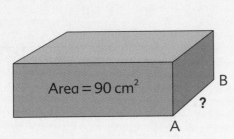

Volume = 360 cm³

AB = cm

(b)

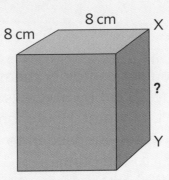

8 cm   8 cm   X

?   Y

Volume = 576 cm³

XY = cm

13. Find the volume of water in each container. Give the answers in liters. (1 L = 1,000 cm³)

(a)

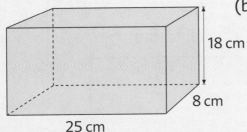

18 cm

8 cm

25 cm

(b)

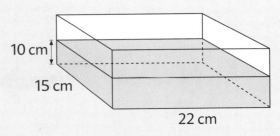

10 cm

15 cm

22 cm

14. The volume of a cube is 125 cm³. Find the length of each edge of the cube.

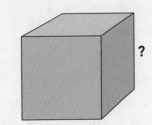

?

15. A rectangular tank, 12 m long and 5 m wide, contains 300 m³ of water when it is full. Find the height of the tank.

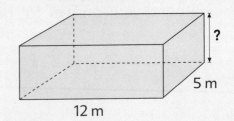

?

5 m

12 m

16. A rectangular container, 40 cm long and 25 cm wide, is filled with 12 L of water. Find the height of the water level in the container.
    (1 L = 1,000 cm³)

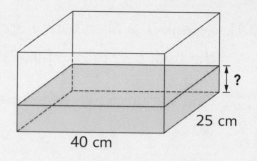

17. A rectangular container measuring 60 cm by 20 cm by 30 cm is filled with 28 L of water. How many more liters of water are needed to fill the container to the brim?
    (1 L = 1,000 cm³)

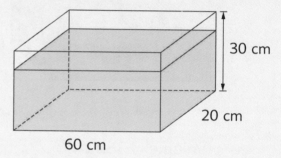

18. Container A was filled with water to its brim. Container B was empty. All the water in Container A is poured into Container B. What is the height of the water level in Container B now?

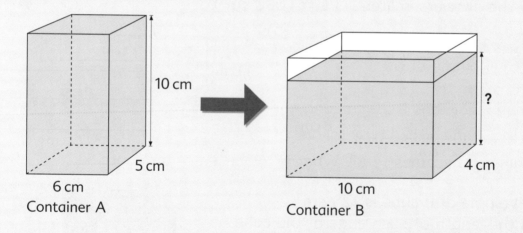

19. A large facility has a floor area of approximately 4,300,000 ft². The height of the building approximately is 109.8 ft. What is the approximate volume of the building? Round your answer to the nearest million cubic feet.

20. Container A is 24 cm long, 10 cm wide, and 40 cm high. It is $\frac{1}{4}$-filled with water. Container B is 30 cm long and 20 cm wide. It is filled with water to a height of 16 cm. When all the water in Container A is added to the water in Container B, Container B becomes $\frac{2}{3}$ full. What is the height of Container B?

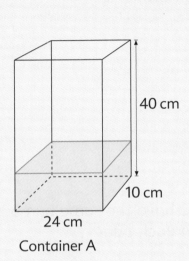

24 cm

Container A

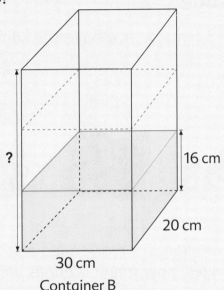

Container B

21. A tank 60 cm by 35 cm is filled with water to a height of 14 cm. If a rock is dropped into the tank, the water level rises by 2 cm. Find the volume of the rock.

22. A rectangular tank is 20 cm long and 20 cm wide. It is filled with water until it is $\frac{1}{2}$ full. When a metal ball of volume 5,600 cm^3 is placed in the container, it becomes $\frac{5}{6}$ full. What is the height of the container?

23. Tom has a rectangular tank with a capacity of 6 L. He placed a metal cube of side 5 cm in the tank and the water level rose to $\frac{2}{3}$ the height of the tank.
(a) What is the volume of the metal cube?
(b) How much water is in the tank?

24. Rectangular prism A measures 2 cm × 3 cm × 5 cm.
Rectangular prism B measures 4 cm × 6 cm × 10 cm.
Judy says that the volume of prism B is twice the volume of prism A. Is Judy correct? Explain.

Review 9, pages 61–65

10 AVERAGE, PLOTS, AND GRAPHS

① Average

These 3 bags do not have the same number of oranges.

If the oranges are rearranged so that the bags have the same number of oranges, how many oranges will there be in each bag?

4 + 9 + 5 = 18

There are 18 oranges altogether.

18 ÷ 3 = 6

There will be 6 oranges in each of these 3 bags.

The **average** of 4, 9, and 5 is 6.

1.

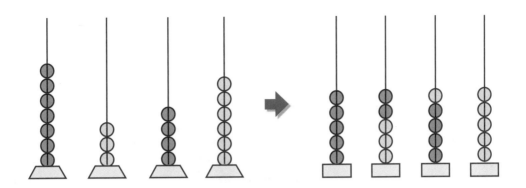

What is the average of 7, 3, 4, and 6?

$7 + 3 + 4 + 6 = 20$

The sum is 20.

First, I find the sum of the 4 numbers.

$20 ÷ 4 = \boxed{}$

Then I divide the sum by 4.

The average is $\boxed{}$.

2. This picture graph shows the number of fish caught by 3 boys. On the average, how many fish did each boy catch?

Andy	🐟🐟🐟🐟🐟
Christian	🐟🐟🐟🐟🐟🐟🐟
Jamal	🐟🐟🐟

$5 + 7 + 3 = 15$

The 3 boys caught 15 fish altogether.

$15 ÷ 3 = \boxed{}$

On the average, each boy caught $\boxed{}$ fish.

3. Sally collected 36 stamps, Mary collected 38 stamps, and Lilian collected 40 stamps. What was the average number of stamps each girl collected?

Total number of stamps collected

= 36 + 38 + 40

= ⬜

To find the average number of stamps, I noticed that I can just move 2 stamps from 40 to 36. Then there will be 38 in each set.

Average number of stamps collected = ⬜

4. The lengths of 5 strings are 1.4 m, 1.8 m, 2 m, 2.6 m, and 3.2 m.
   (a) What is the total length of the 5 strings?
   (b) What is the average length?

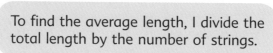

To find the average length, I divide the total length by the number of strings.

5. The table on the right shows the points Ron scored.
   (a) What is his total score for the 4 tests?
   (b) What is his average score?

Test A	68
Test B	76
Test C	78
Test D	88

6. Find the average of each of the following.
   (a) 18, 16, 19, 21, 17, and 11
   (b) 142, 133, 131, 131, and 143
   (c) $27, $63, $80, and $99
   (d) 2.62 m, 2.08 m, 3.9 m, and 0.96 m
   (e) 4.81 gal, 3.52 gal, 3.59 gal, and 2 gal
   (f) 9.5 in., 7.25 in., 11.9 in., 4.11 in., and 6.09 in.

Exercise 1, pages 66–69

7. A taxi driver traveled a total distance of 1,659 km in 7 days. Find the average distance he traveled per day.

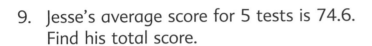

1,659 km ÷ 7

8. Martin saved $1,032 last year. What is the average amount he saved per month?

9. Jesse's average score for 5 tests is 74.6. Find his total score.

74.6 × 5

10. Warner spent an average of $4.65 per day for 8 days. How much did he spend altogether?

11. The average mass of 3 boxes is 1 kg 400 g. Find the total mass.

Total mass = 3 × 1 kg 400 g

= ⬜ kg ⬜ g

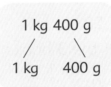

1 kg 400 g
  /   \
1 kg   400 g

12. The total mass of 4 cats is 5 kg 200 g. Find the average mass.

Average mass = 5 kg 200 g ÷ 4

= ⬜ kg ⬜ g

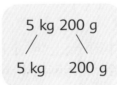

5 kg 200 g
  /   \
5 kg   200 g

13. David took 15 minutes 20 seconds to cycle a distance of 2 km. If he traveled at the same average speed, how long would he take to cycle 1 km?

14. Peter took an average of 2 minutes 45 seconds to cycle 1 km. How long would he take to cycle 3 km?

Exercise 2, pages 70—71

15. The average height of two boys is 1.55 m. The height of one boy is 1.62 m. What is the height of the other boy?

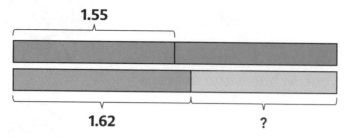

1.55 × 2 = 3.1

The total height of the two boys is 3.1 m.

3.1 − 1.62 =

The height of the other boy is ▢ m.

I solve this in a different way.
1.62 − 1.55 = 0.07
1.55 − 0.07 = 1.48

16. The average cost of 3 books is $4.50. The average cost of two of the books is $3.90. Find the cost of the third book.

$4.50 × 3 = $13.50

The total cost of the 3 books is $13.50.

$3.90 × 2 = $7.80

The total cost of two of the books is $7.80.

$13.50 − $7.80 = $▢

The cost of the third book is $▢.

17. An average of 145 people visited a 4-day exhibition in the first 3 days. Another 205 people visited the exhibition on the fourth day. What is the average number of visitors per day?

18. The average number of chickens on 4 farms is 8,900. Two of these farms have 6,180 chickens and 3,960 chickens respectively. How many chickens do the other farms have altogether?

Exercise 3, page 72

② Line Plots

Manufacturers of sportswear claim that clothing made of synthetic fibers, such as polyester or nylon, "wick" moisture away from the body better than cotton.

Jake did some experiments to see if the claim was true. He soaked 8 square patches of each type of fabric, polyester, nylon, and cotton, in water. For each square of fabric, he draped a corner on the rim of a large glass. He then placed a smaller glass next to the large glass as shown.

To "wick" means to draw off liquid.

As time passes, water moves through the fabric and drips into the smaller glass. The water collected in the smaller glass is the moisture that has been wicked away from the fabric. After 24 hours, Jake measured the water in the smaller glass using a measuring cup.

Fabric	Water wicked away in cups							
Polyester	$1\frac{3}{4}$	$1\frac{7}{8}$	$1\frac{1}{8}$	$1\frac{7}{8}$	$1\frac{3}{4}$	$1\frac{1}{2}$	$1\frac{3}{4}$	$1\frac{5}{8}$
Nylon	$\frac{7}{8}$	1	$1\frac{1}{8}$	$\frac{3}{4}$	$1\frac{1}{4}$	1	$1\frac{1}{4}$	$1\frac{3}{8}$
Cotton	0	0	0	0	0	0	0	0

He then created a line plot of the data.

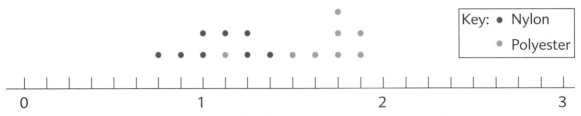

**Amount of water wicked away by nylon
or polyester fabric in 24 h in cups**

(a) Which fabric was better at wicking water?

(b) What is the difference between the highest value and
the lowest value obtained for each fabric?

(c) Look at the line plot. Without calculating, estimate the
average amount of water wicked away by each fabric.

1. What is the average amount of water wicked away by the
nylon fabric squares?

$$\left(\frac{7}{8} + 1 + 1\frac{1}{8} + \frac{3}{4} + 1\frac{1}{4} + 1 + 1\frac{1}{4} + 1\frac{3}{8}\right) \div 8 = \boxed{}$$

> To add the list of fractions, I looked for
> ways to make ones. $6 + 2 + \frac{1}{4} + \frac{3}{8} = \boxed{}$

The average amount of water wicked away by the
nylon fabric is $\boxed{}$.

2. What is the average amount of water wicked away by the
polyester fabric squares?

$$\left(1\frac{3}{4} + 1\frac{7}{8} + 1\frac{1}{8} + 1\frac{7}{8} + 1\frac{3}{4} + 1\frac{1}{2} + 1\frac{3}{4} + 1\frac{5}{8}\right) \div 8 = \boxed{}$$

> I converted each fraction to a
> decimal and then found the average.
> $1.75 + 1.875 + 1.125 \ldots$

The average amount of water wicked away by the
polyester fabric is $\boxed{}$.

3. (a) What data value is represented the most for the polyester fabric?

   (b) What is the difference between this value and the average value?

   (c) What data value has the greatest effect on causing the difference in (b)?

4. Jake then squeezed all the water he could out of each fabric piece and measured the amount of water.

Fabric	Water squeezed out in cups							
Polyester	$\frac{1}{8}$	$\frac{1}{4}$	$\frac{1}{8}$	$\frac{1}{4}$	$\frac{3}{8}$	$\frac{1}{4}$	$\frac{1}{4}$	$\frac{1}{8}$
Nylon	$\frac{1}{2}$	$1\frac{1}{8}$	$\frac{5}{8}$	1	$\frac{5}{8}$	$\frac{3}{4}$	$\frac{7}{8}$	$\frac{3}{4}$
Cotton	2	$2\frac{3}{8}$	$2\frac{1}{2}$	$2\frac{3}{4}$	$1\frac{3}{4}$	$2\frac{1}{4}$	$1\frac{7}{8}$	$2\frac{1}{2}$

   (a) Make a line plot of the results.
       Include a title and labels.

   (b) Which fabric absorbs the most water?
       Which one absorbs the least?

   (c) Find the difference between the highest and lowest data value for each type of fabric.

   (d) Find the average for each type of fabric.

5. Discuss with your classmates any conclusions you can make from Jake's results.

Exercise 4, pages 73–74

3 Coordinate Graphs

Students are assigned a seat before the exam starts. The desks are arranged in rows and columns.

Aaron	Cory	Steve	Jeremy	Sharon	Amy
Zoe	Tyler	Gary	Ana	Jasmine	Nathan
Sophia	Domingo	Shayla	Andre	Claude	Isobel
Tammy	Lorenzo	Sheila	Gabrielle	Lesley	Sam
David	Roxy	Jericho	Alex	Terry	Tia

Rows (label at left)

Columns

Front

Each student was given a card with a pair of numbers. The first number was to tell which column from the left, and the second number which row up from the front. Sheila's card says (3, 2), so her seat is column 3, row 2. Jeremy's card says (4, 5) so his seat is column 4, row 5.

(a) Who occupied the following seats?

(2, 3)   (6, 4)   (3, 5)   (4, 1)   (3, 3)

(1, 1)   (2, 5)   (4, 4)   (6, 2)   (5, 3)

(b) Which seats did the following students occupy?

Tyler   Amy   Alex   Isobel   Tia

Aaron   Lorenzo   Sharon   Andre   David

(c) Do the pairs of numbers (4, 2) and (2, 4) refer to the same seat? If not, who occupies seat (4, 2) and (2, 4)?

1. The following map shows the locations of some attractions in a park.

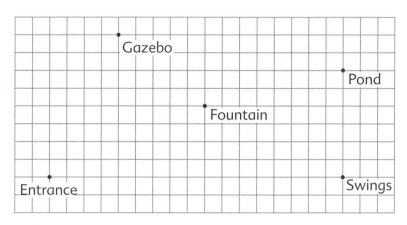

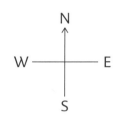

The fountain is located 9 units east and 4 units north of the entrance. We can write its position as (9, 4).

(a) The position of the swings is (⬚ , ⬚).

(b) The position of the gazebo is (⬚ , ⬚).

(c) The position of the pond is (⬚ , ⬚).

2. The following shows positions of places on a farm on a **coordinate grid**.

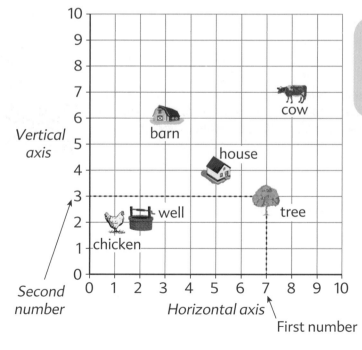

A **coordinate grid** has two number lines or **axes**, a **horizontal axis** and a **vertical axis**. The **origin** is 0 on both number lines.

The tree is at the position (7, 3).

What is the position of each of the following:

(a) Barn

(b) Cow

(c) House

(d) Chicken

(e) Well

The location of a point on the grid can be represented with a set of two distances from the origin, first the horizontal distance and then the vertical distance.

3.

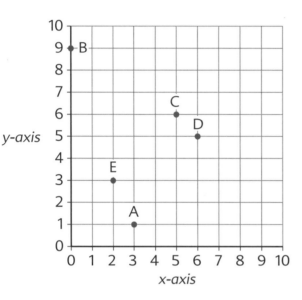

y-axis

x-axis

The horizontal axis is called the **x-axis**. The vertical axis is called the **y-axis**. The position of a point on the graph is given by an **ordered pair**. The numbers in an ordered pair are called the **coordinates**. The first number is called the **x-coordinate** and the second number is called the **y-coordinate**.

Which point corresponds to each ordered pair?

(a) (2, 3)

(b) (0, 9)

(c) (5, 6)

(d) (6, 5)

Exercise 5, pages 75–76

4. Each square on this graph is 1 unit.

   (a) Find the length of line segments AB and CD.

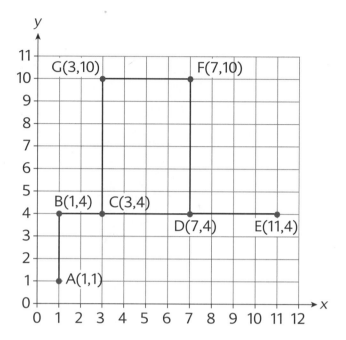

   (i) AB = ☐ units   (ii) CD = ☐ units

   (b) The ☐-coordinate of the endpoint of line segment FD
       are the same.

       Line segment FD is parallel to the ☐-axis.

       To find the length of FD, we subtract the ☐-coordinates.

   (c) What is the distance from Point C to a point at (3, 18)?

5. Two points, P and Q, are at coordinates (10, 20) and (15, 20).

   (a) A line connecting P and Q is parallel to the ☐-axis.

   (b) P and Q are ☐ units apart.

6. A rectangle has coordinates (2, 3), (2, 10), (6, 10), and (6, 3) on a
   grid with 1-cm squares. What is the perimeter of the rectangle?

Exercise 6, pages 77–78

④ Line Graphs

The length, *l*, of a rectangle is 2 cm more than the width, *w*.

$l = w + 2$

w	l	(w, l)
1	3	(1, 3)
2	4	(2, 4)
3	5	(3, 5)
4	6	(4, 6)

We can write the width and the length as an ordered pair, and show the values on a coordinate grid.

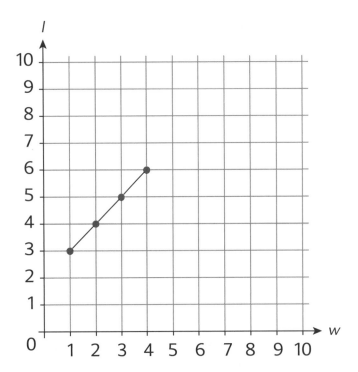

When the points are connected, we get a straight line.

How can we use the grid to find the length of the rectangle if the width is 6 cm?

1. (a) The first four terms of Sequence A are 1, 3, 5, and 7. Each term is obtained by adding 2 to the previous term. Copy and complete the following table of the first 8 terms of this sequence.

An ordered list of numbers is called a **sequence**. Each number in sequence is called a **term**.

Term (x)	1	2	3	4	5	6	7	8
Number (y)	1	3	5	7				
(x, y)	(1, 1)	(2, 3)	(3, 5)					

(b) Sequence B starts at 1 and is generated by adding 4 to the previous term. Copy and complete the following table for the first 8 terms of this sequence.

Term (x)	1	2	3	4	5	6	7	8
Number (y)	1	5	9					
(x, y)	(1, 1)	(2, 5)	(3, 9)					

(c) Copy and complete the graph below, extending the y-axis. Plot both sets of ordered pairs on the same graph. Connect the points for each set.

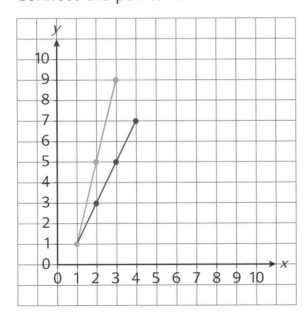

Both lines increase. Going from left to right, both the x-coordinate and the y-coordinate get larger.

97

(d) What type of line can be used to connect the points for each set of data?

(e) Find the distance between each set of points for each term. Copy and complete the following table.

Term	1	2	3	4	5	6	7	8
Distance between the points in Sequence 1 and Sequence 2	0	2	4					

(f) What can you conclude about the distance between each corresponding point in the two sequences as the term increases?

2. (a) A restaurant has triangular tables. Each table can seat 3 people at most. For larger parties, the tables are pushed together to form a row. Complete the table below.

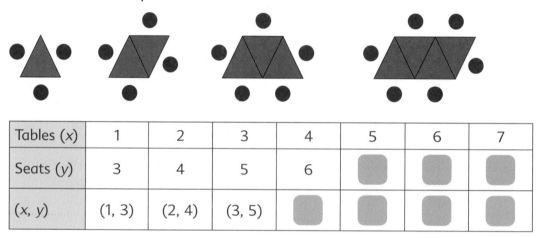

Tables (x)	1	2	3	4	5	6	7
Seats (y)	3	4	5	6			
(x, y)	(1, 3)	(2, 4)	(3, 5)				

(b) Another restaurant has square tables, each of which can seat 4 people. Complete the table below.

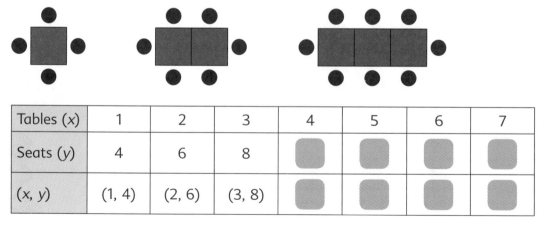

Tables (x)	1	2	3	4	5	6	7
Seats (y)	4	6	8				
(x, y)	(1, 4)	(2, 6)	(3, 8)				

98

(c) Copy and complete the graph below, extending the y-axis.
Plot both sets of ordered pairs on the same graph.
Connect the points for each set.

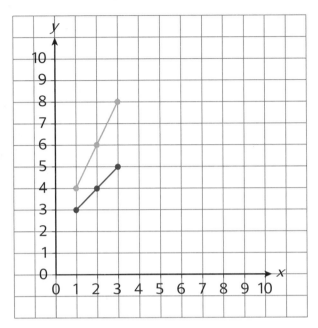

(d) What type of line can be used to connect the points for each set of data?

(e) How far apart are the points for each line when $x = 3$?

(f) How far apart will the points for each line be when $x = 15$?

3. (a) Use the graph to complete the table for line a on the next page.

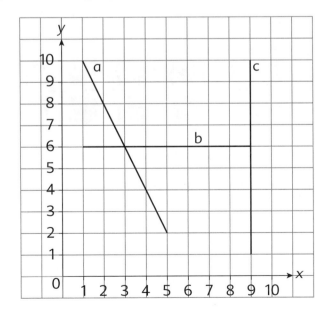

x	1	2	3	4	5	6
y	10	8	6	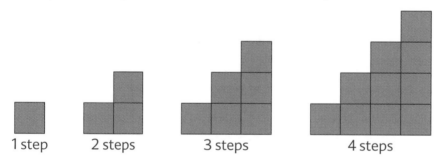		
(x, y)						

(b) In line *a*, how does *y* change each time x increases by 1?

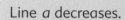

(c) List some coordinates for lines *b* and *c*.

(d) In line *c*, the ▢-coordinate stays the same.

(e) In line *b*, the ▢-coordinate stays the same.

4. Squares, with sides 1 cm, are used to make a pattern with steps. Complete the pattern for 5, 6, and 7 steps.

1 step 2 steps 3 steps 4 steps

(a) Complete the following table.

Number of steps	1	2	3	4	5	6	7	8
Perimeter (cm)	4	8	12					
Area (cm²)	1	3	6					

(b) What is the perimeter if the number of steps is 10?

(c) What is the area if the number of steps is 10?

(d) Form the ordered pairs (number of steps, perimeter) and
    (number of steps, area) for the number of steps 1 through 8.
    Copy and complete the graph below, extending the y-axis.
    Plot both sets of ordered pairs on the same graph.

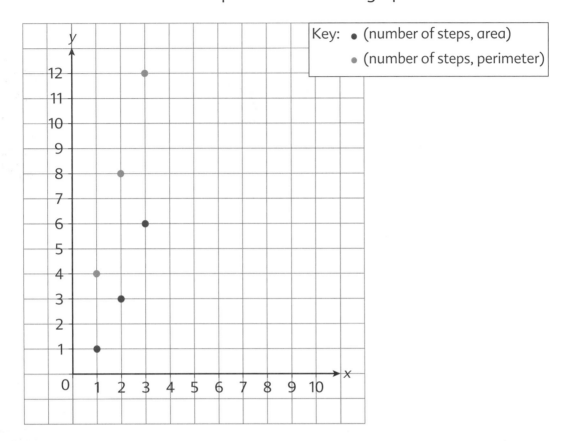

Key: • (number of steps, area)
     • (number of steps, perimeter)

(e) Connect the points for each set of ordered pairs.
    What kind of line must be drawn to connect the
    points for (number of steps, area)?

Exercise 7, pages 79–83

101

5. Mr. Clark recorded the number of people in his store by the hour from 5 P.M. to 10 P.M.

Time	5 P.M.	6 P.M.	7 P.M.	8 P.M.	9 P.M.	10 P.M.
Number of people	50	75	125	200	100	0

For every time value, there is a value for the number of people. Each data is a pair of numbers.

He then drew a line graph to show the same information.

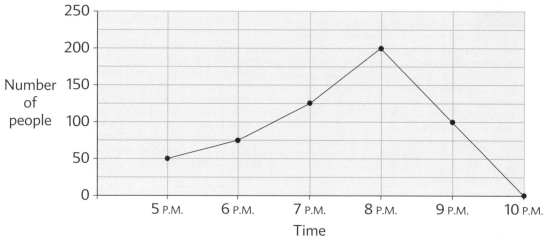

We can use a graph to see how the number of people changes over time. The axes are not the same.

(a) In this graph, the x-axis is used for time.
What is the y-axis used for?

(b) At what time was there the greatest number of people in the store?

(c) Over what time period did the number of people increase?

(d) Over what time period did the number of people decrease?

(e) What was the increase in the number of people from 7 P.M. to 8 P.M.?

(f) What was the decrease in the number of people from 8 P.M. to 9 P.M.?

6. Danny created a line graph for the data he collected for the high and low temperatures over a 10-day period.

Day	1	2	3	4	5	6	7	8	9	10
High temperature (°F)	73	74	75	74	79	82	81	85	83	86
Low temperature (°F)	62	64	62	63	65	68	66	70	69	70

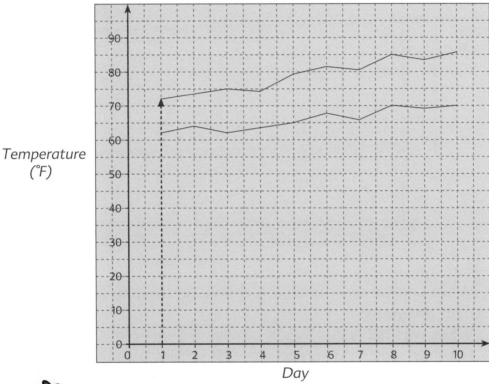

Temperature (°F)

Day

The point for the high temperature for the first day is at 73 degrees F.

We can use a line graph to see if data changes over time.

(a) What values are on the horizontal axis?
(b) What values are on the vertical axis?
(c) How does the data change over time?

7. This line graph shows the height in inches for a boy from the age of 5 years to 12 years.

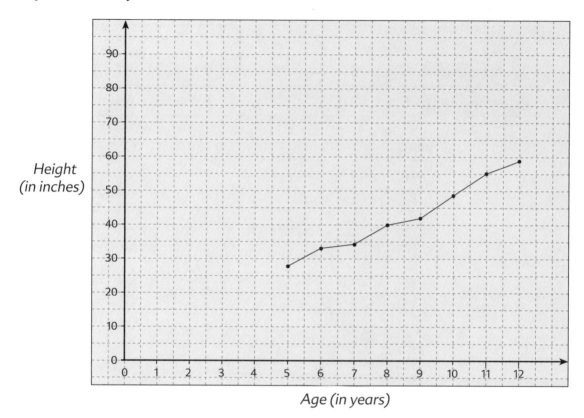

Height (in inches)

Age (in years)

(a) What can we say about the change in the boy's height over the years?

(b) What was his height when he was 8 years old?

(c) How old was he when he was 35 in. tall?

(d) Between which ages did the greatest increase in height take place?

8. This graph shows the average value of a car versus its mileage.

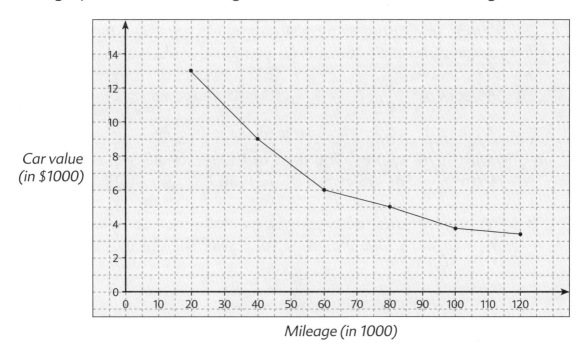

Car value
(in $1000)

Mileage (in 1000)

(a) According to the graph, what happens to the value of the car the more it is driven?

(b) About how much could the owner sell the car for if the mileage on the car is 70,000?

(c) The car is being sold for $10,000.
The mileage is 50,000.
Is this a good deal for the person buying the car?

Exercise 8, pages 84–89

1. The average age of a group of 11 girls is 14 years. The average age of these girls and their coach is 16 years. How old is their coach?
   (A) 30 years old   (B) 34 years old
   (C) 38 years old   (D) 41 years old

2. A rectangle has coordinates at (2, 7), (2, 2), (5, 2), and (5,7) on a grid with 1 cm squares. The area of the rectangle is _____.
   (A) 14 cm²   (B) 15 cm²   (C) 16 cm²   (D) 20 cm²

3. This line graph shows the weekly sales made by a company during a 4-week trade show. Use the graph to answer the questions which follow.

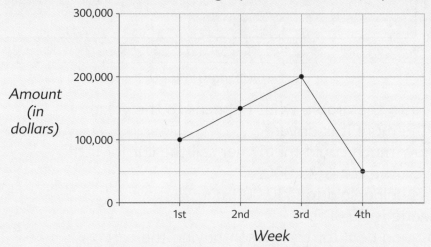

   (a) The increase in sales from the first to the third week is _____.
       (A) $100,000   (B) $150,000
       (C) $200,000   (D) $300,000

   (b) The overall decrease in sales over the 4 weeks is _____.
       (A) $50,000   (B) $100,000
       (C) $150,000   (D) $200,000

4. Select True or False.
   (a) The average of 33, 29, 42, 35, and 22   True / False
       is $30 + \left(\dfrac{(3 - 1 + 12 + 5 - 8)}{5} \right)$.

   (b) The average of $2\frac{1}{2}$ in., $4\frac{2}{5}$ in., $6\frac{3}{4}$ in., and $5\frac{3}{8}$ in.   True / False
       is $\dfrac{(2.5 + 4.2 + 6.75 + 5.6)}{4}$ in..

106

5. Select True or False.
   (a) A point at (5, 6) is 6 units away from   True / False
       the y-axis.
   (b) Points (4, 3), (5, 5), and (6, 7) can be   True / False
       joined with a straight line.

6. Find the average of each of the following.
   (a) 12.5, 36.2, 30.4, and 26.1
   (b) $1.35, $4.82, $3.05, $2.70, and $2.13
   (c) 3.5 kg, 3.8 kg, 4.1 kg, and 5 kg
   (d) 4.6 L, 6.4 L, 5.8 L, and 3.8 L
   (e) 2.62 m, 2.08 m, 3.9 m, and 0.96 m
   (f) 12.2 km, 25.6 km, 9.5 km, and 30.3 km
   (g) 4.81 gal, 3.52 gal, 3.59 gal, and 2 gal
   (h) $9\frac{1}{2}$ in., $7\frac{1}{4}$ in., $11\frac{3}{8}$ in., $4\frac{3}{4}$ in., and $6\frac{1}{8}$ in.

7. The average of 63, 74, ▢ , and 85 is 82.

   What is the missing number in the ▢ ?

8. The average of five numbers is 40.
   If four of the numbers are 18, 27, 37, and 50,
   what is the fifth number?

9. Rowley traveled 5,460 km in 3 months.
   What was the average distance he traveled per month?

10. A man has 6 packages.
    Their average mass is 18 kg.
    Find the total mass of the 6 packages.

11. 4 people had lunch together.
    They spent an average of $3.75 each.
    What was the total cost of the lunch?

12. The average of 3 numbers is 45.
    If the average of 2 of the numbers is 27,
    what is the third number?

13. (a) Make a line plot of the following data.

$2\frac{2}{5}$	$2\frac{1}{2}$	$1\frac{7}{10}$	$2\frac{4}{5}$	$2\frac{1}{10}$	$2\frac{5}{10}$
$1\frac{6}{10}$	$1\frac{7}{10}$	$2\frac{1}{2}$	$2\frac{9}{10}$	$1\frac{8}{10}$	$2\frac{1}{5}$

(b) Find the difference between the smallest and largest value.

(c) Find the average of the data.

14.

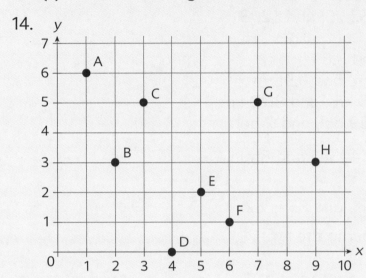

(a) Point D is at ____.

(b) Point G is at ____.

(c) Point ____ is at (6, 1).

(d) Point ____ is at (9, 3).

15. The bar graph shows the daily attendance of a class of 40 students.

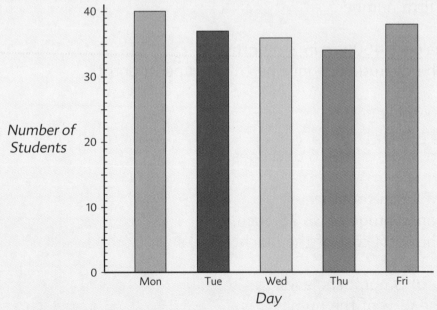

(a) On which day was the attendance the lowest?

(b) What fraction of the students were absent on Friday?

(c) What was the average daily attendance?

16.

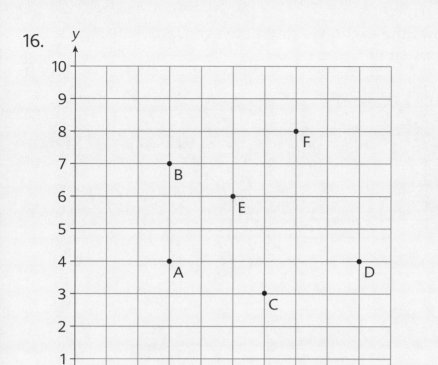

(a) What is the ordered pair for Point C?
(b) What point is at (7, 8)?
(c) What is the distance between the points A and D in units?
(d) Which coordinates, the first or second, of the ordered pair do you subtract to find the distance from A to B?
(e) Point Z is at (5, 12). How far is it from Point E?
(f) Another point that would be on a line formed by the points A, E, and F is (9, ☐).

(g) Complete the table for the ordered pair (x, y) corresponding to the points A, E, and F.

Points	A	E	F
x			
y			

17. This line graph shows the exchange rate between US dollars and Singapore dollars some years ago.

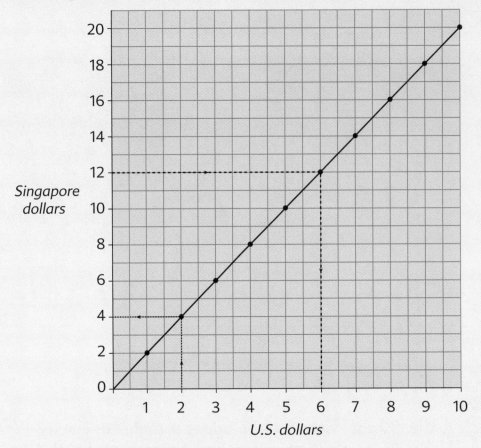

Singapore dollars

U.S. dollars

(a) How many Singapore dollars would be exchanged for 9 US dollars?

(b) How many US dollars would be exchanged for 10 Singapore dollars?

(c) How many US dollars would be exchanged for 16 Singapore dollars?

(d) How many Singapore dollars would be exchanged for 30 US dollars?

18. Tank A and Tank B are the same size. Every minute, 25 gal of water is added to Tank A and 30 gal of water is added to Tank B.
    (a) Complete the table.

Time (min)	1	2	3	4	5	6
Amount of water (gal) in Tank A	25					
Amount of water (gal) in Tank B	30					

    (b) Write an ordered pair for each tank with the values of time from 1 to 6 minutes as the x-coordinate.
    (c) Copy the graph below and plot each set of ordered pairs.

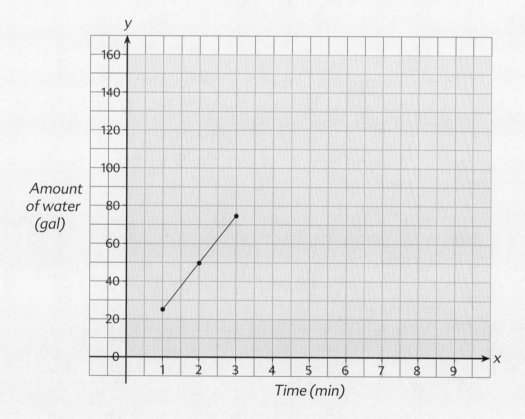

    (d) Compare the two lines.
        Which tank will be filled more quickly?
    (e) Use the graph to approximate how long it will take for each tank to have 80 gal of water. Round your answers to one decimal place.

19. This graph shows the amount of gas Jake bought in the last 6 months. Use the graph to answer the questions which follow.

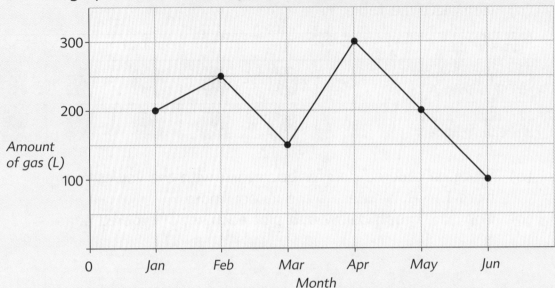

(a) Find the average amount of gas he bought each month.
(b) If 1 L of gas cost $1.15, how much less money did he spend on gas in March than in February?

20. This graph shows the number of cars Mr. Shaw sold in the first six months of a year.

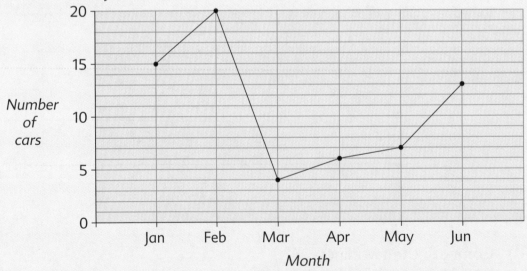

(a) What was the decrease in the number of cars sold between February and March?
(b) What was the total number of cars sold in the six months?
(c) Mr. Shaw received a commission of $1,000 for every car he sold. How much commission did he receive in February?

21. This line graph shows the sales of T-shirts over 5 months.

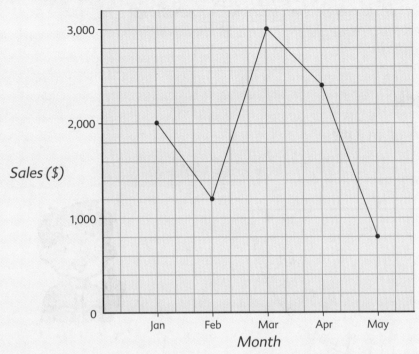

(a) What was the increase in sales from February to March?
(b) What was the average monthly sales?
(c) If each T-shirt was sold for $4 in April, how many T-shirts were sold that month?

22. Under what circumstances are line plots useful for displaying data? Do you think making measurements in fractions is a useful way to gather data that will be used to perform various calculations? Explain your answers.

Review 10, pages 90—95

1 Looking Back

What is the size of m∠m?

$m\angle m = 180° + 45°$

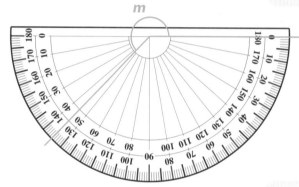

$m\angle m = 360° - 135°$

Measure m∠n.

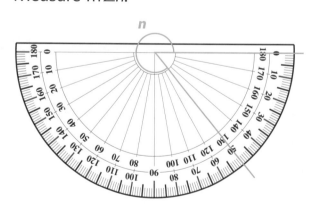

Which method should I use?

1. Estimate. Then find each of the following marked angles by measurement.

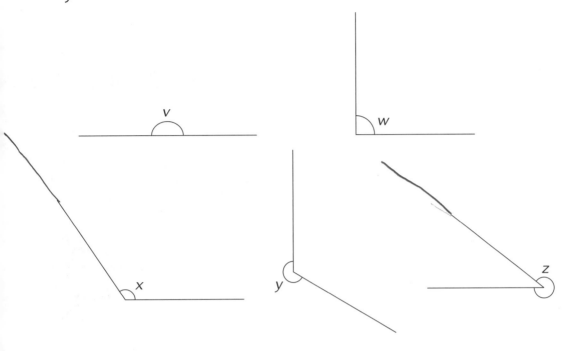

Which of these angles is a right angle?

Exercise 1, pages 96—99

2.

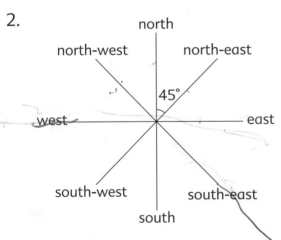

(a) You start facing north and turn clockwise to south-east.
What angle do you turn through?
(b) You start facing west and turn counterclockwise to south-west.
What angle do you turn through?

3. (a) You start facing north-west and turn clockwise through 90°. Which direction are you facing?
    (b) After turning counterclockwise through 225°, you end up facing east. Which direction were you facing at the start?

Exercise 2, pages 100—101

4. (a) Measure the marked angle in the following polygons.

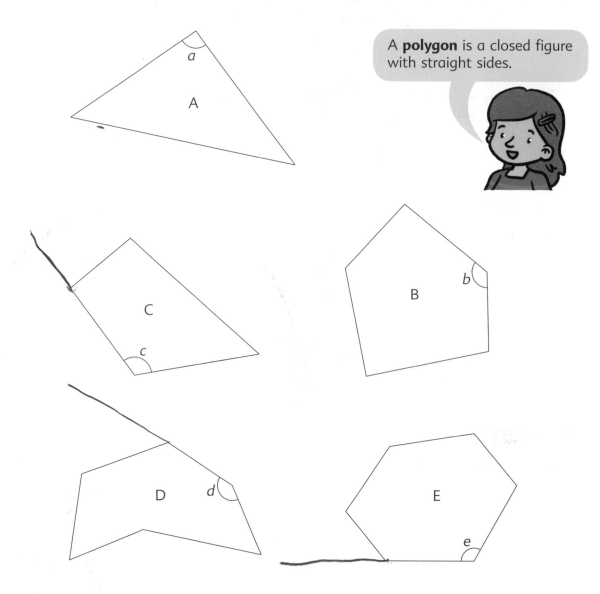

A **polygon** is a closed figure with straight sides.

(b) Which figure is a quadrilateral?
(c) What are the names of the other figures?

5. Do you remember?

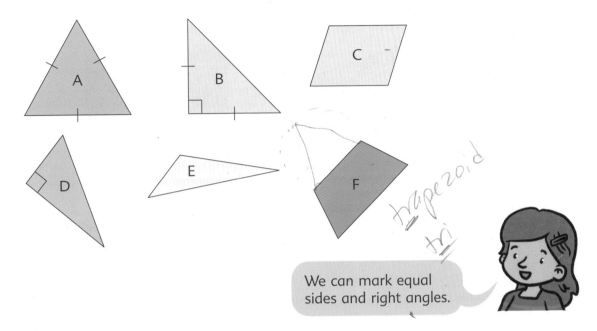

We can mark equal sides and right angles.

(a) **Isosceles** triangles have at least two equal sides.
Which triangles are isosceles?

(b) **Equilateral** triangles have all sides equal.
Which triangles are equilateral?

(c) **Scalene** triangles have no equal sides.
Which triangles are scalene?

(d) **Right** triangles have one right angle.
Which triangles are right triangles?

(e) **Acute** angles are smaller than right angles.
Which of these triangles have only acute angles?

(f) **Obtuse** angles are greater than right angles but smaller than straight lines.
Which of these triangles have an obtuse angle?

An equilateral triangle is also an isosceles triangle.

117

6. Do you remember?

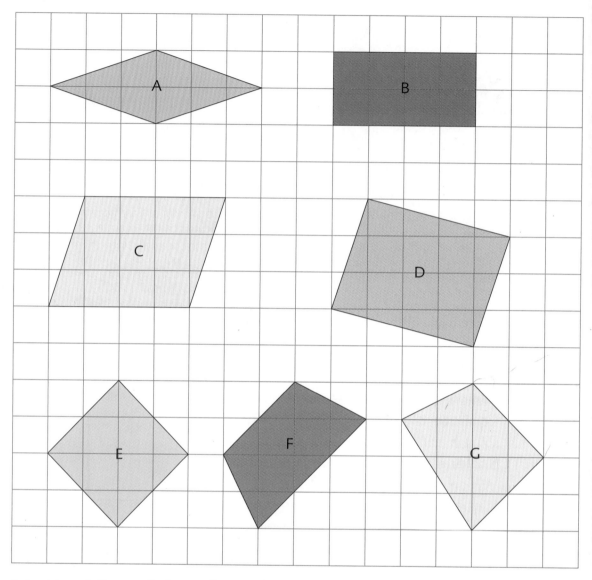

(a) **Quadrilaterals** have four sides.
Which of these figures are quadrilaterals?

(b) A **trapezoid** has at least one pair of parallel lines.
Which of these figures are trapezoids?

(c) A **parallelogram** has two pairs of parallel lines.
Which of these figures are parallelograms?

(d) A **rectangle** is a parallelogram with four right angles.
Which of these figures are rectangles.

(e) A **square** is a rectangle with four equal sides.
Which of these figures are squares.

(f) A **rhombus** is a quadrilateral with four equal sides.
Which of these figures are rhombuses?

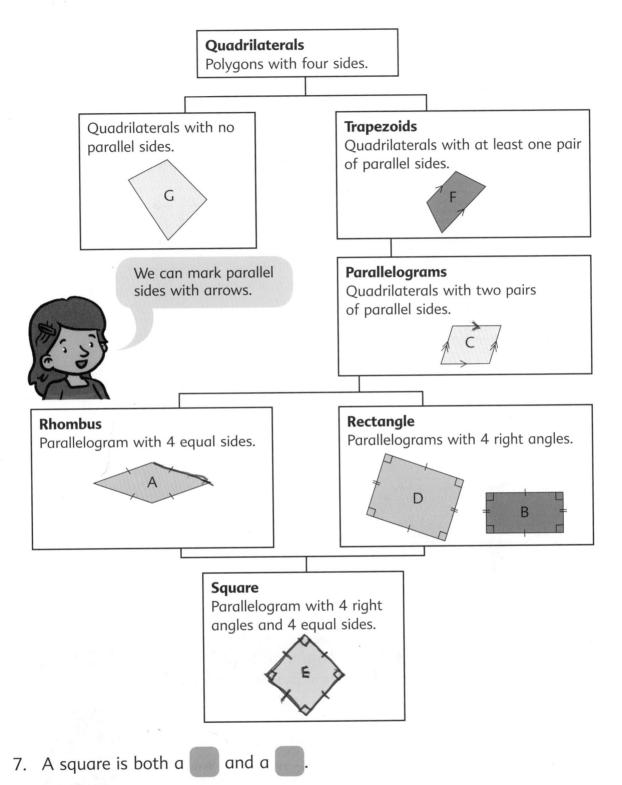

7. A square is both a ▢ and a ▢.

8. Use graph paper. Draw some additional examples of trapezoids that are not parallelograms.

9. Use graph paper. Draw some additional examples of parallelograms that are not rhombuses or rectangles.

Exercise 3, pages 102–104

2 Finding Unknown Angles

When two straight lines cross, they form two pairs of
vertically opposite angles.

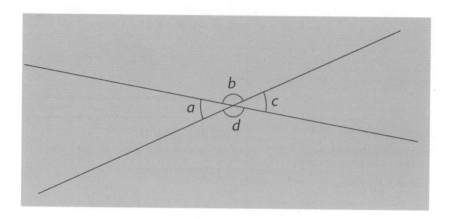

Measure the unknown angles.

$m\angle a = 34°$

$m\angle b = \boxed{}°$

$m\angle c = \boxed{}°$

$m\angle d = \boxed{}°$

$m\angle a = m\angle c$

$m\angle b = m\angle d$

∠a and ∠c are vertically opposite angles.

∠b and ∠d are also vertically opposite angles.

Vertically opposite angles are **equal**.

∠p, ∠q and ∠r are **angles on a straight line**.
Measure the unknown angles.

m∠p = 50°

m∠q = °

m∠r = °

m∠p + m∠q + m∠r = °

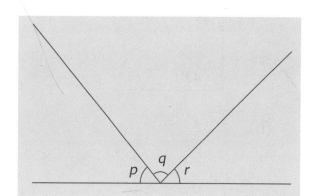

AOB is a straight line.

The sum of the angles on a straight line is **180°**.

∠x, ∠y and ∠z are **angles at a point**.
Measure the unknown angles.

m∠x = 60°

m∠y = °

m∠z = °

m∠x + m∠y + m∠z = °

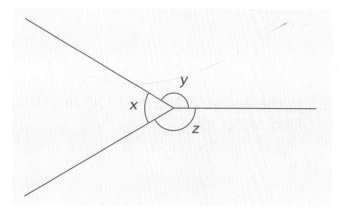

The 3 marked angles meet at a common point.

The sum of the angles at a point is **360°**.

1. Find the unknown marked angle in each of the following.

(a)

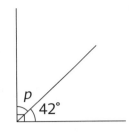

$m\angle p = 90° - 42° =$ °

(b)

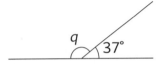

$m\angle q = 180° - 37° =$ °

(c)

$m\angle r = 360° - 15° =$ °

2. The figure shows 4 angles formed by two straight lines. If $m\angle w = 46°$, find $m\angle x$, $m\angle y$, and $m\angle z$.

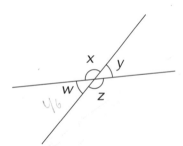

3. In the figure, AOB and COD are straight lines. Find $m\angle COB$.

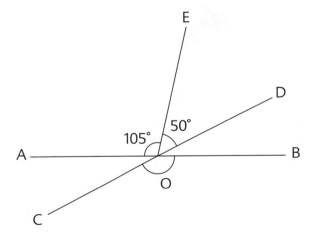

4. In the figure, ABC is a straight line.
   m∠ABD = 35° and m∠EBC = 55°. Find m∠DBE.

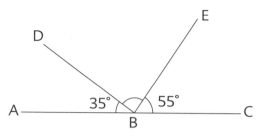

m∠DBE = 180° − 35° − 55°

5. In the figure, find m∠x.

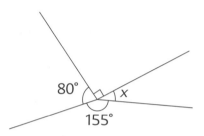

m∠x = 360° − 90° − 80° − 155°

6. In the figure, find m∠m and m∠n.

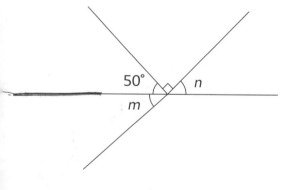

∠m and ∠n are vertically opposite angles.

7. Find the unknown marked angles.

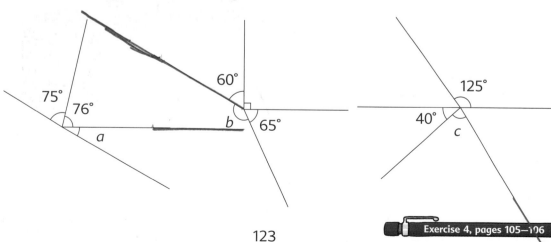

Exercise 4, pages 105–106

③ Finding Unknown Angles in Triangles

Trace and cut out this triangle.

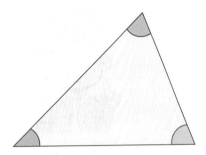

Then cut the triangle into 3 pieces as shown.

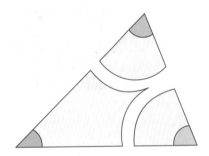

What do you notice when you arrange the 3 pieces like this?

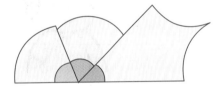

What is the sum of the three angles?

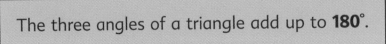

The three angles of a triangle add up to **180°**.

1. Measure and add up the angles in each triangle.

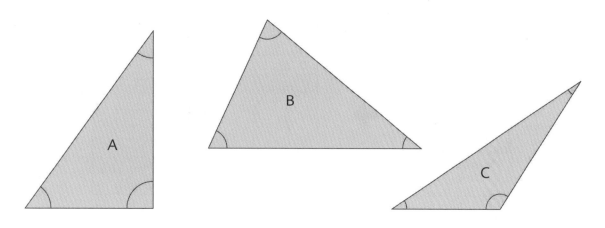

2. In Triangle ABC, m∠ABC = 82° and m∠BAC = 54°.
   Find m∠BCA.

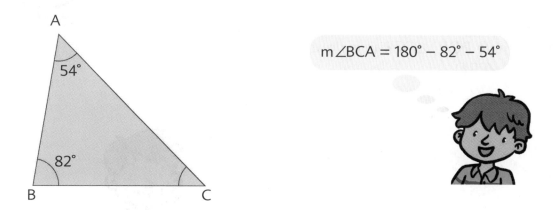

m∠BCA = 180° − 82° − 54°

3. Find the unknown marked angle in each triangle.

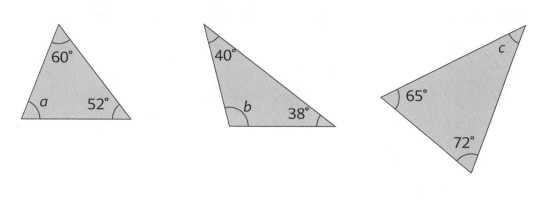

Exercise 5, page 107

4. Fold a right-angled triangle as shown.

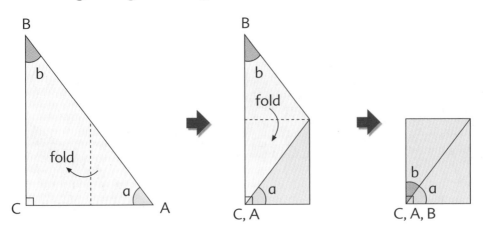

What do you notice?

When one angle of a triangle is a right
angle, the other two angles add up to 90°.

m∠BCA = 90°
m∠a + m∠b = 90°

5. In triangle PQR, ∠QPR is a right angle and m∠PQR = 57°.
   Find m∠PRQ.

m∠PRQ = 90° − 57°

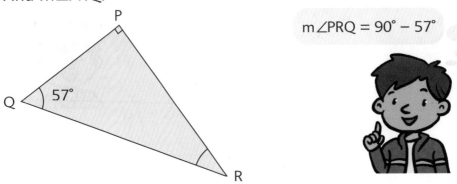

6. Which of the following figures are right triangles?

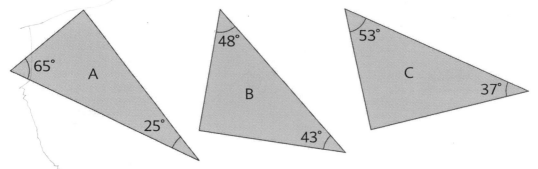

126

Exercise 6, page 108

7. In triangle ABC, BC is extended to D.

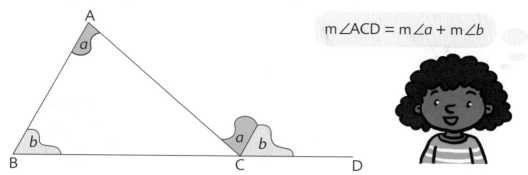

$m\angle ACD = m\angle a + m\angle b$

∠ACD is an **exterior angle** of the triangle.
∠a and ∠b are **interior opposite angles** of ∠ACD.

> The **exterior angle** of a triangle is equal to the sum of its **interior opposite angles**.

8. In triangle XYZ, YZ is extended to P, m∠ZXY = 50° and m∠XYZ = 34°. Find m∠XZP.

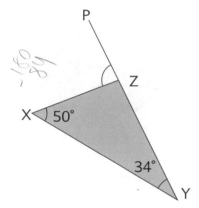

$m\angle XZP = 50° + 34°.$

9. In each figure, ACD is a straight line.
   Find the unknown marked angle.

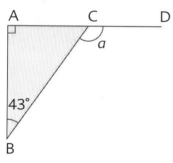

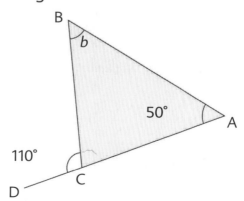

Exercise 7, page 109

10. Fold an **isosceles triangle** in half as shown.
    What do you notice?

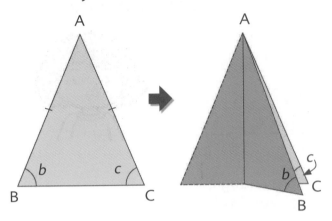

The angles opposite the equal sides are equal.

11. In triangle XYZ, ∠YXZ = ∠YZX.
    Is the triangle an isosceles triangle?

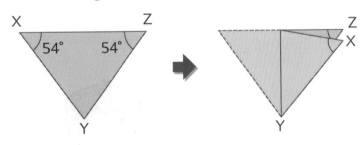

XYZ is an isosceles triangle.

12. Which of the following are isosceles triangles?

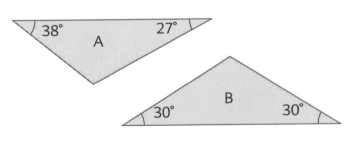

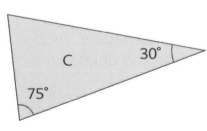

13.

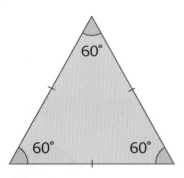

An **equilateral triangle** has 3 equal sides and 3 equal angles. Each angle is 60°.

Which of the following are **equilateral triangles**?

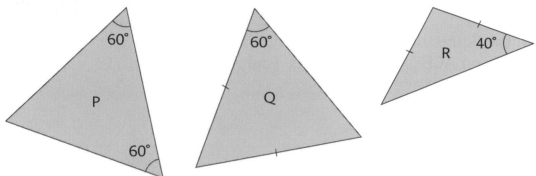

P

Q

R
40°

Exercise 8, pages 110–111

14. In triangle ABC, AB = AC and m∠ABC = 35°.
Find m∠ACB and m∠BAC.

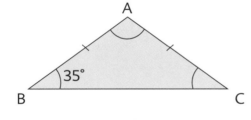

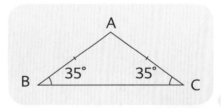

m∠ACB = 35°

m∠BAC = 180° − 35° − 35° = ⬜°

129

15. In triangle PQR, QR = PR and m∠PQR = 65°.
    QRS is a straight line. Find m∠PRS.

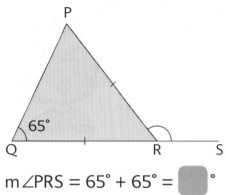

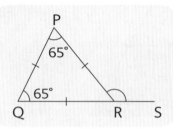

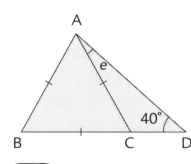

m∠PRS = 65° + 65° = ☐°

16. In the figure, AB = AC and m∠DCE = 75°.
    BCD and ACE are straight lines. Find m∠ABC.

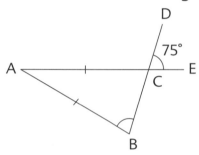

17. BCD is a straight line in each figure.
    Find the unknown marked angles.

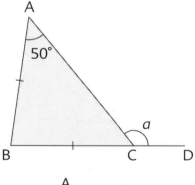

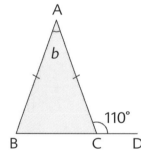

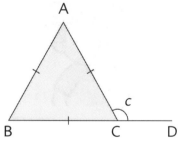

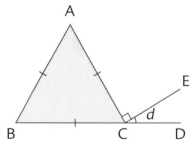

Exercise 9, pages 112–113

4 Finding Unknown Angles in Quadrilaterals

Draw a quadrilateral. Color each angle in a different color.

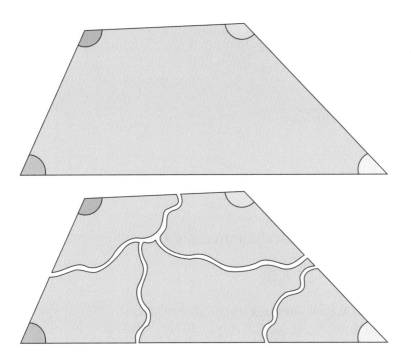

Then, tear off the angles.
Place the angles together at a point.

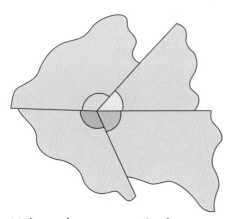

What do you notice?

The angles of a quadrilateral add up to **360°**.

1.

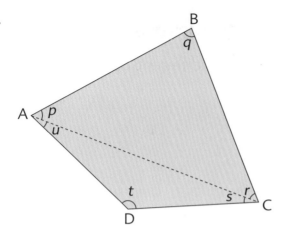

Sum of angles of triangle ABC = $m\angle p + m\angle q + m\angle r$

$$= \boxed{}°$$

Sum of angles of triangle CDA = $m\angle s + m\angle t + m\angle u$

$$= \boxed{}°$$

Sum of angles of quadrilateral ABCD = $m\angle p + m\angle q + m\angle r +$
$m\angle s + m\angle t + m\angle u$

$$= \boxed{}°$$

2. Find the unknown marked angles in each quadrilateral.

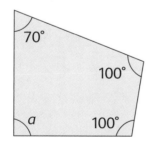

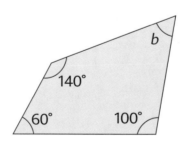

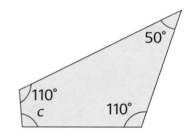

Exercise 10, page 114

3. Trace and cut out this parallelogram.

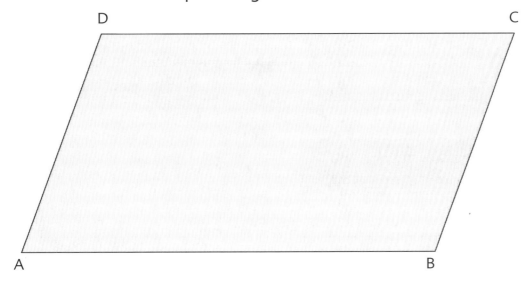

Then cut the parallelogram into two pieces and match the angles as shown.

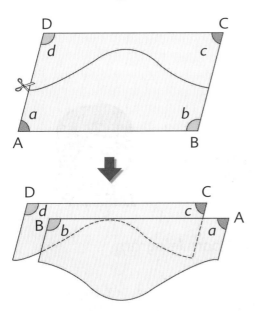

What do you notice?

$$m\angle a = m\angle c$$
$$m\angle b = m\angle d$$

The opposite angles of a parallelogram are **equal**.

4. (a)

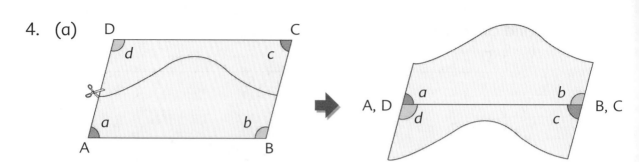

$$m\angle a + m\angle d = 180°$$
$$m\angle b + m\angle c = 180°$$

(b)

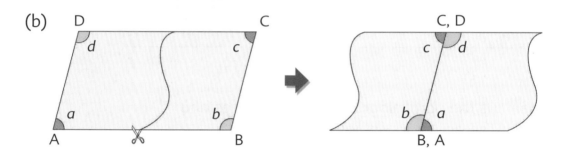

$$m\angle a + m\angle b = 180°$$
$$m\angle c + m\angle d = 180°$$

Each pair of angles between two parallel sides add up to **180°**.

5. Find the unknown marked angle in each parallelogram.

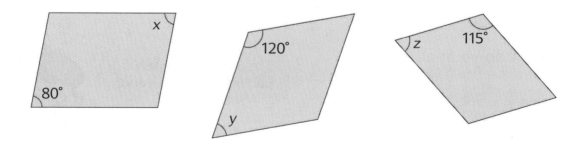

Exercise 11, pages 115–116

6. In the figure, ABCD is a rectangle and m∠DAC = 26°.
   Find m∠BAC.

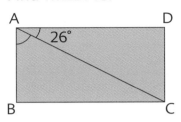

m∠BAD = 90°

7. Find the unknown marked angle in each rhombus.

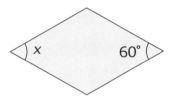 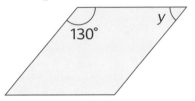 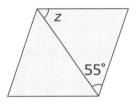

8. In trapezoid ABCD, AD // BC.
   Find m∠ABC and m∠DCB.

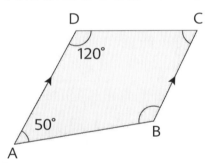

Each pair of angles
between two parallel
sides add up to 180°.

m∠ABC = 180° − 50°

   = ⬜°

m∠DCB = 180° − 120°

   = ⬜°

9. Find the unknown marked angle in each trapezoid.

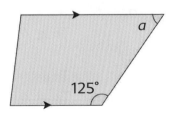 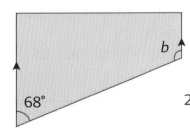 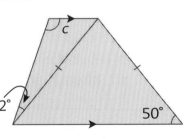

135

Exercise 12, pages 117–119

1. Which of these marked angles is an obtuse angle?

(A)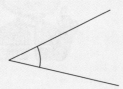

(B)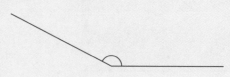

(C)

(D)

2. Use the figure to answer each of the following.

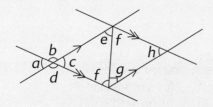

(a) $m\angle a + m\angle d = m\angle c + $ _____

    (A) $m\angle a$ (B) $m\angle b$ (C) $m\angle e$ (D) $m\angle f$

(b) $m\angle e + m\angle f = $ _____

    (A) $m\angle a$ (B) $m\angle c$ (C) $m\angle d$ (D) $m\angle g$

(c) $m\angle f + m\angle g = $ _____

    (A) $m\angle a$ (B) $m\angle b$ (C) $m\angle h$ (D) $m\angle e$

3. Select True or False.

    (a) A trapezoid has only one pair of parallel sides.   True / False

    (b) When a line is drawn from opposite angles in a parallelogram, it always divides the parallelogram into two isosceles triangles.   True / False

    (c) In a parallelogram, the angles next to each other are always equal.   True / False

    (d) A rhombus does not have any right angles.   True / False

4. Select True or False.
   (a) All acute triangles are isosceles triangles.   True / False
   (b) The sum of angles on a straight line is 90°.   True / False
   (c) The adjacent angles in an equilateral triangle
       are always equal to each other.   True / False

5. Estimate. Then find the marked angles by measurement.

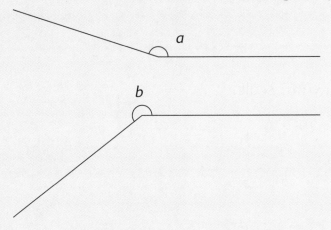

6. In each of the following figures, not drawn to scale, find m∠x.
   AOB and COD are straight lines.
   (a)   (b)

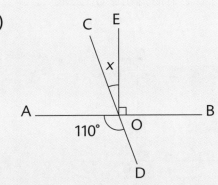

7. In each of the following figures, not drawn to scale, find m∠x.
   (a)   (b)

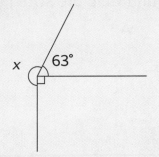
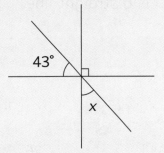

8. In each of the following figures, not drawn to scale, find m∠x.

(a) ABC is a straight line.

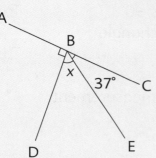

(b)

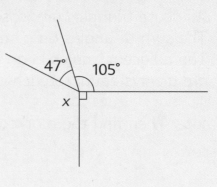

9. The figure shown is not drawn to scale.
   Find the measure of ∠ABC.

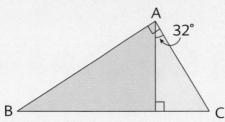

10. ABCD is a square. BDE is a straight line.
    Find the measure of ∠w.

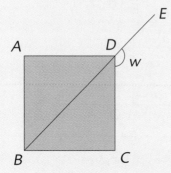

11. In each of the following figures, not drawn to scale, find m∠y.

(a) BCD is a straight line.

(b) ABC and CDE are straight lines

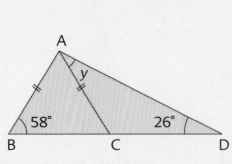

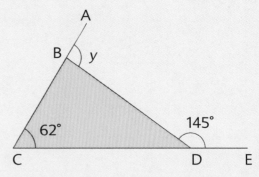

12. In the figure, ACE and BCD are straight lines. AB = BC.
    The figure is not drawn to scale. Find m∠x.

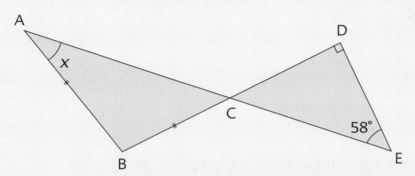

13. (a) Find the area of quadrilateral ABEC.
    (b) Find the measure of ∠ACE.
    (c) Find the measure of ∠CED.

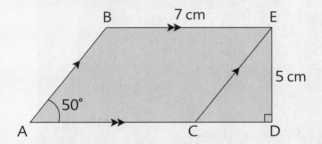

14. In quadrilateral ABCD, m∠ABC = 95°, m∠BCD = 83°, and m∠CDA = 62°.
    What is the measure of ∠DAB?

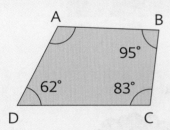

15. Which angle is bigger? Explain your answer.

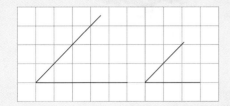

Review 11, pages 120–125

12 PERCENTAGE

1 Percent

There are 100 seats in a theater.
55 seats are occupied.

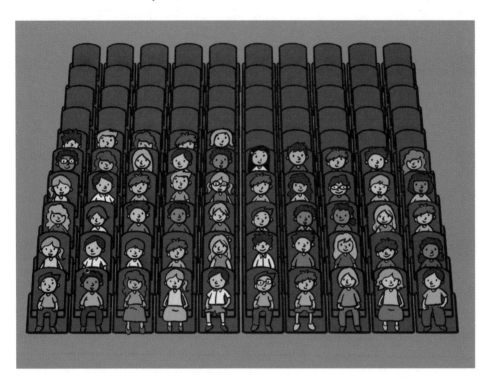

55% of the seats are occupied.

We read 55% as **55 percent**.

55% means **55 out of 100**.

55% is another way of writing $\frac{55}{100}$ or 0.55.

1. 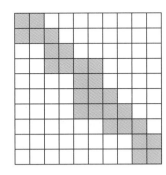 The whole is divided into 100 equal parts.
27 parts are shaded.
What **percentage** of the whole is shaded?

27 out of 100 is %.

2. What percentage of the whole is shaded?

(a)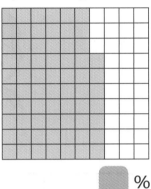

 %

(b)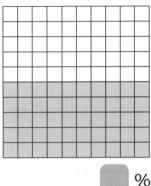

%

(c)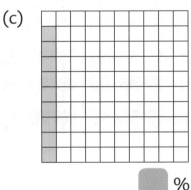

%

(d)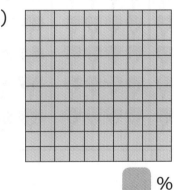

%

3. Write each of the following as a percentage.

(a) 33 out of 100   (b) 20 out of 100   (c) 5 out of 100

4. Express each fraction as a percentage.

(a) $\frac{23}{100}$ (b) $\frac{45}{100}$ (c) $\frac{36}{100}$ (d) $\frac{75}{100}$

(e) $\frac{40}{100}$ (f) $\frac{70}{100}$ (g) $\frac{3}{10}$ (h) $\frac{5}{10}$

Change the denominator to 100. Hence, $\frac{3}{10} = \frac{}{100}$

Exercise 1, pages 126–127

5. Express 0.35 as a percentage.

$$0.35 = \frac{35}{100}$$

$$= \boxed{} \%$$

6. Express each decimal as a percentage.
    (a) 0.07   (b) 0.02   (c) 0.85   (d) 0.7

7. Express 43% as a decimal.

$$43\% = \frac{43}{100}$$

$$= \boxed{}$$

Write $\frac{43}{100}$ as a decimal.

8. Express each percentage as a decimal.
    (a) 28%   (b) 88%   (c) 30%   (d) 5%

9.
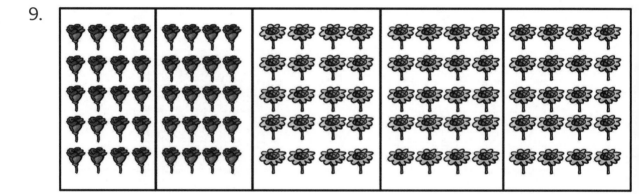

40% of the flowers are roses.
What fraction of the flowers are roses?

$$40\% = \frac{40}{100}$$

$$= \boxed{}$$

Write $\frac{40}{100}$ in its simplest form.

$\boxed{}$ of the flowers are roses.

10. Express each percentage as a fraction in its simplest form.
    (a) 10%   (b) 80%   (c) 25%   (d) 75%
    (e) 5%   (f) 8%   (g) 4%   (h) 2%

Exercise 2, pages 128–130

② Writing Fractions as Percentages

Mr. Goldberg has painted $\frac{3}{4}$ of a wall.

What percentage of the wall has he painted?

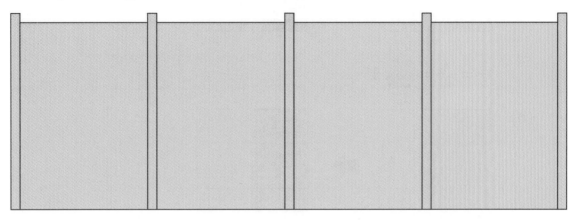

Method 1:

$$\frac{3}{4} = \frac{75}{100}$$

$$= \boxed{} \%$$

Method 2:

$$\frac{3}{4} = \frac{3}{4} \times 100\%$$

$$= \boxed{} \%$$

1 whole is 100%.

$\frac{3}{4}$ is $\frac{3}{4}$ of 100%.

He has painted % of the wall.

1. Express each fraction as a percentage.

   (a)
   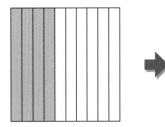 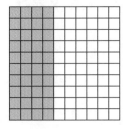

   $\frac{2}{5} = \frac{4}{10} = $ ⬚ %

   (b)
   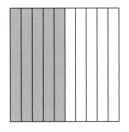 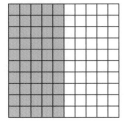

   $\frac{1}{2} = \frac{5}{10} = $ ⬚ %

2. Express 7 out of 25 as a percentage.

   Method 1:

   $\frac{7}{25} = \frac{28}{100} = $ ⬚ %

   Method 2:

   $\frac{7}{25} = \frac{7}{25} \times 100\% = $ ⬚ %

3. Limei has 20 apples. Of them, 14 are red apples.
   What percentage of the apples are red apples?

   $\frac{14}{20} = $ ⬚ %

   $\frac{14}{20}$ is 14 out of 20.

   ⬚ % of the apples are red apples.

4. Express each fraction as a percentage.

   (a) $\frac{1}{4}$ (b) $\frac{2}{5}$ (c) $\frac{4}{5}$ (d) $\frac{9}{20}$

   (e) $\frac{13}{20}$ (f) $\frac{6}{25}$ (g) $\frac{14}{25}$ (h) $\frac{41}{50}$

Exercise 3, pages 131–132

5. Express 180 out of 300 as a percentage.

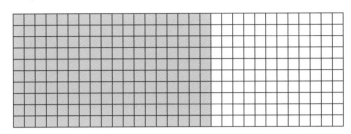

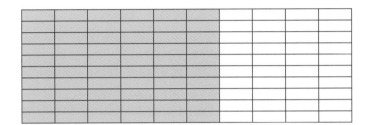

Method 1:

$$\frac{180}{300} = \frac{60}{100} = \boxed{} \%$$

Method 2:

$$\frac{180}{300} = \frac{180}{300} \times 100\% = \boxed{} \%$$

6. There are 200 children at a concert. 98 of them are boys.
   What percentage of the children are boys?

   $$\frac{98}{200} = \boxed{} \%$$

   $\frac{98}{200}$ is 98 out of 200.

   $\boxed{}$ % of the children are boys.

7. Express each fraction as a percentage.

   (a) $\frac{8}{200}$ (b) $\frac{36}{200}$ (c) $\frac{60}{300}$ (d) $\frac{129}{300}$

   (e) $\frac{40}{400}$ (f) $\frac{128}{400}$ (g) $\frac{20}{500}$ (h) $\frac{255}{500}$

Exercise 4, pages 133–134

8. What percentage of each of the following bars is shaded?
   (Use the percentage scale to help you.)

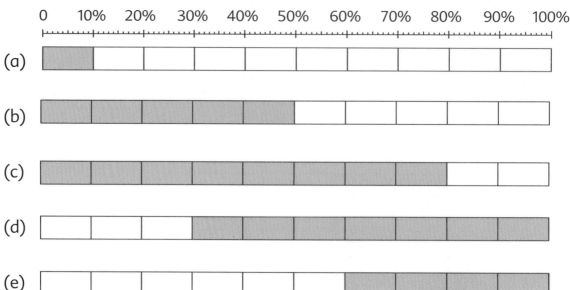

   0   10%   20%   30%   40%   50%   60%   70%   80%   90%   100%

   (a)

   (b)

   (c)

   (d)

   (e)

1 whole is 100%.

9. Of the pies which Mrs. Goodman made, $\frac{3}{4}$ were apple pies.

   (a) What percentage of the pies were apple pies?

   $\frac{3}{4} = \frac{3}{4} \times 100\% = 75\%$

   [ ] % of the pies were apple pies.

   (b) What percentage of the pies were not apple pies?

   $100\% - 75\% = $ [ ] %

   [ ] % of the pies were not apple pies.

10. Of 25 children, 7 are boys.
    (a) What percentage of the children are boys?
    (b) What percentage of the children are girls?

11. Sam had $750. He spent $300 and saved the rest.
    What percentage of the money did he save?

146

Exercise 5, pages 135–136

❸ Percentage of a Quantity

There were 500 people at a concert. Of them, 30% were children. How many children were there at the concert?

Method 1:

500

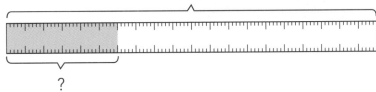

?

1% of 500 = $\frac{1}{100}$ × 500

= 5

30% of 500 = 5 × 30

=

30% of the whole is shaded.

There were ▢ children at the concert.

Method 2:

30% of 500 = $\frac{30}{100}$ × 500

= ▢

30% = $\frac{30}{100}$

There were ▢ children at the concert.

1. 0 10% 20% 30% 40% 50% 60% 70% 80% 90% 100%

$200

1 unit = $\frac{\$200}{10}$

= $20

(a) 10% of $200 = $20

(b) 20% of $200 = $▢

(c) 50% of $200 = $▢

(d) 80% of $200 = $▢

2. In a school, 120 students took part in a physical fitness test.
   90% of them passed the test.
   How many students passed the test?

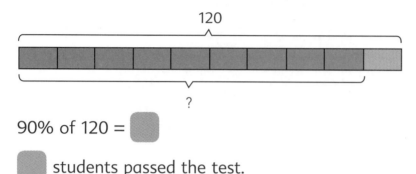

90% of 120 = ⬜

⬜ students passed the test.

3. Lindsey bought a refrigerator which cost $800.
   She had to pay 8% sales tax on $800.
   How much was the sales tax?

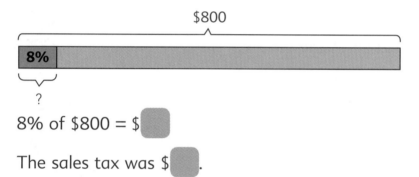

8% of $800 = $⬜

The sales tax was $⬜.

4. The area of a garden is 60 m².
   7% of it is taken up by a pond.
   What is the area of the pond?

5. There were 50 words in a spelling test.
   Sally spelled 90% of them correctly.
   How many words did she spell correctly?

6. Find the value of each of the following.
   (a) 5% of 300   (b) 8% of 200
   (c) 20% of 60 kg   (d) 25% of 40 m
   (e) 40% of 70 km   (f) 75% of 400 g

Exercise 6, pages 137–138

7. William had $500. He spent 24% of his money on transport and 36% on food.

    (a) What percentage of his money was left?

$500

| 24% | 36% | ? |

$100\% - 24\% - 36\% = 40\%$

1 whole is 100%.

⬜% of his money was left.

    (b) How much money was left?

$500

| 24% | 36% | 40% |

?

$40\% \times \$500 = \$$ ⬜

$⬜ was left.

8. There were 400 members in a swimming club.
    12% of the members were children.
    The rest were adults. How many adults were there?

Method 1:

$100\% - 12\% = 88\%$

88% of the members were adults.

$88\% \times 400 =$ ⬜

There were ⬜ adults.

Method 2:

Number of children $= 12\% \times 400 = 48$

Number of adults $= 400 - 48 =$ ⬜

There were ⬜ adults.

9. There are 20 workers in a library. 55% of them are females.
   How many male workers are there?

10. Tasha earns $1,350 monthly. She saves 30% of the money.
    How much does she save each month?

Exercise 7, pages 139—140

11. Ahmad has $2,700 in a savings bank.
    The interest rate is 3% per year.
    How much money will he have in the bank after 1 year?

    Interest = 3% of $2,700

    = $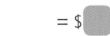

    Find the interest
    for 1 year first.

    Amount of money in the bank after 1 year = $2,700 + Interest

    = $

    He will have $ [ ] in the bank after 1 year.

12. A man bought a refrigerator at a discount of 12%.
    Its usual price was $900.
    How much did he pay for the refrigerator?

    Discount = 12% of $900

    Discount = $ [ ]

    Amount of money paid = $900 − Discount

    = $ [ ]

    He paid $ for the refrigerator.

13. Joanne's monthly salary was $1,500 in May.
It was increased by 8% in June.
What was her salary in June?

Increase = 8% of $1,500

Increase in salary = $⬜

Salary in June = $1,500 + Increase

= $⬜

Her salary in June was $⬜.

14. There were 400 members in a chess club last year.
The membership was decreased by 5% this year.
How many members are there this year?

Decrease = 5% of 400

Decrease = ⬜

Number of members this year = 400 − Decrease

= ⬜

There are members this year.

15. A swimming club had 720 members last year.
This year the membership increased by 5%.
Find the number of members this year.

16. Mary bought a swimsuit which cost $50.
In addition, she had to pay 3% sales tax.
How much did she pay for the swimsuit?

17. The usual price of a camera was $190.
At a sale, it was sold at a discount of 30%.
What was the sale price?

Exercise 8, pages 141–143

1. 0.0206 expressed as a percentage is _____.

   (A) 0.0206%   (B) 0.206%   (C) 2.06%   (D) 2.06%

2. Three students were absent out of a class of 45. What percentage of students were present?

   (A) Less than 3%

   (B) Less than 6%

   (C) Less than 90%

   (D) More than 90%

3. 15% expressed as a fraction is _____.

   (A) $\frac{3}{4}$ (B) $\frac{3}{10}$ (C) $\frac{3}{20}$ (D) $\frac{3}{25}$

4. 25% of a number is 100. What is the number?

   (A) 25   (B) 50   (C) 200   (D) 400

5. Select True or False.

   (a) 20% of 180 = 30% of 120   True / False

   (b) 30 cm as a percentage of 2 m is 30%.   True / False

6. Select True or False.

   (a) 20% is the same as $\frac{1}{5}$.   True / False

   (b) A 10% increase of a 10% increase of 100 is 100.   True / False

7. Write each of the following as a percentage.

   (a) 14 out of 100

   (b) 6 out of 100

8. Express each fraction as a percentage.

   (a) $\frac{15}{20}$ (b) $\frac{150}{200}$ (c) $\frac{260}{400}$

9. What percentage of each figure is shaded?

(a)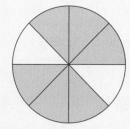

(b)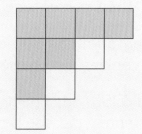

10. Express 80% as a decimal.

11. Express 48% as a fraction in its simplest form.

12. (a) Express 20 out of 25 as a percentage.

(b) Express 90 out of 200 as a percentage.

13. Express each of the following as a percentage.

(a) 0.9   (b) 0.08   (c) $\frac{29}{50}$ (d) $\frac{27}{300}$

14. Find the value of each of the following.

(a) 7% of 160   (b) 80% of 98 kg   (c) 15% of $21

15. Find the value of each of the following.

(a) 3% of $60   (b) 10% of 450 g   (c) 35% of 120 m

16. A school has four classes in 5th grade. The table shows the number of boys and girls in each class.

Class	Number of boys	Number of girls
A	23	15
B	18	20
C	17	19
D	20	18

(a) How many more boys than girls are there in 5th grade?

(b) What percentage of the students in 5th grade are boys?

17. Mary has 200 coins. 98 of them are commemorative coins. What percentage of the coins are commemorative coins?

18. There are 200 families in an apartment complex. 186 of them own computers. What percentage of the families own computers?

19. Mrs. Washington made 500 cookies. She sold 96% of them. How many cookies did she sell?

20. Marisol had $350. She spent 35% of the money on a pressure cooker. How much money did she have left?

21. There are 1,800 students in a school. 60% of them are boys. How many more boys than girls are there?

22. In a school, 150 students took a mathematics test. 98% of them passed the test. How many students passed the test?

23. The usual price of a motorcycle was $3,600. Eric bought the motorcycle at a discount of 15%. How much did he pay?

24. Rupert made 250 donuts. He sold 90% of them. How many donuts did he have left?

25. The usual price of a pair of shoes was $45. It was sold at a discount of 20%. Find the selling price.

26. Lynn deposits $5,000 in a bank which pays 4% interest per year. How much money will she have in the bank after 1 year?

27. The cost of a TV set was $640. Patrick sold it at 10% above the cost price. Find the selling price.

28. A book costs $6. Sam sold it at a price 25% higher than the usual price. What was the selling price of the book?

29. The cost price of a bookcase was $180. It was sold at an amount 15% lower than the cost price. Find the selling price.

30. An electronics store advertises that everything is on 20% discount. During a special weekend sale, the store gave an additional 30% discount. Simon gave the cashier $50 for a radio which originally costs $100. However, the cashier asked Simon for another $6. Why?

Review 12, pages 144–146

13 RATE

1 Rate

A machine fills 60 similar bottles of syrup in 5 minutes.
How many such bottles of syrup can it fill in one minute?

The machine fills the same number of bottles every minute.

In 5 minutes, the machine fills 60 bottles.
In 1 minute, it fills ⬜ bottles.

$60 \div 5 = 12$

The machine fills the bottles at the **rate** of 12 bottles per minute.
This means the machine fills 12 bottles every minute.

1. Robert is paid $20 for working 4 hours.
   How much is he paid per hour?

   $20 ÷ 4 = 5$

   The rate is $5 per hour.

   He is paid $5 per hour.

2. Water is flowing from a tap at the rate of 100 L every 4 minutes.
   Find the rate of flow of water in liters per minute.

   $100 ÷ 4 =$

   100 L in 4 min

    L in 1 min

   The rate of flow of water is L per minute.

3. A machine makes similar toy cars at the rate of 120 per minute.
   How many such toy cars will it make in 6 minutes?

   $120 × 6 =$

   120 toy cars in 1 min

    toy cars in 6 min

   It will make toy cars in 6 minutes.

4. A lamp can flash 5 times per minute. At this rate,
   how many times can it flash in 30 minutes?

   $5 × 30 =$

   5 times in 1 min

    times in 30 min

   The lamp can flash  times in 30 minutes.

Exercise 1, pages 147—148

5. Water is flowing from a tap at the rate of 25 gal per minute.

    (a) How much water can be collected from the tap in 5 minutes?

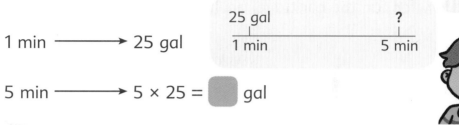

1 min ⟶ 25 gal

5 min ⟶ 5 × 25 = ▢ gal

▢ gal of water can be collected from the tap in 5 minutes.

    (b) How long will it take to fill a container of capacity 100 gal?

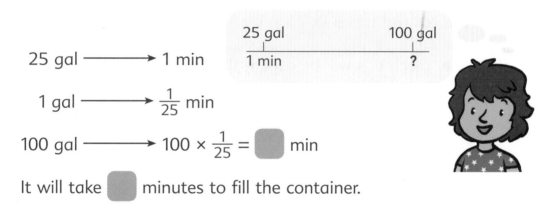

25 gal ⟶ 1 min

1 gal ⟶ $\frac{1}{25}$ min

100 gal ⟶ 100 × $\frac{1}{25}$ = ▢ min

It will take ▢ minutes to fill the container.

6. Mrs. Ricci types 45 words per minute.
    At this rate, how long will she take to type 135 words?

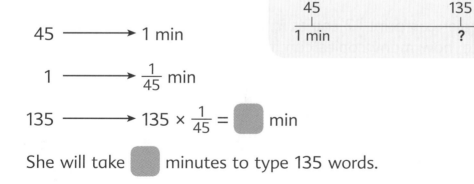

45 ⟶ 1 min

1 ⟶ $\frac{1}{45}$ min

135 ⟶ 135 × $\frac{1}{45}$ = ▢ min

She will take ▢ minutes to type 135 words.

Exercise 2, pages 149–150

7. A car can travel 96 km on 8 L of gas.

The rate is  km per liter.

(a) How far can the car travel on 15 L of gas?

8 L $\longrightarrow$ 96 km

1 L $\longrightarrow$ $\frac{96}{8}$ = 12 km

15 L $\longrightarrow$ 15 × 12 = ⬜ km

The car can travel ⬜ km on 15 L of gas.

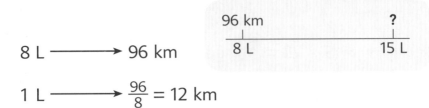

(b) How much gas will be used if the car travels a distance of 120 km?

96 km $\longrightarrow$ 8 L

1 km $\longrightarrow$ $\frac{8}{96}$ L

120 km $\longrightarrow$ 120 × $\frac{8}{96}$ = ⬜ L

⬜ L of gas will be used.

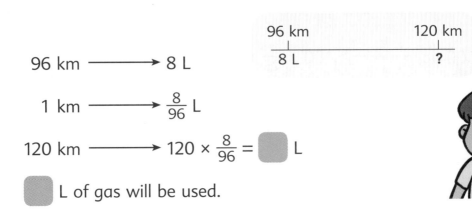

8. A photocopier can print 12 copies in 48 seconds.
At this rate, how many copies can it print in 1 minute?

48 s $\longrightarrow$ 12

1 s $\longrightarrow$ $\frac{12}{48}$

60 s $\longrightarrow$ 60 × $\frac{12}{48}$ = ⬜

It can print ⬜ copies in 1 minute.

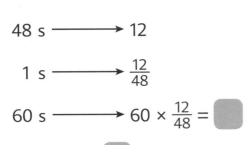

Exercise 3, pages 151–152

9. The table shows the rates of charges at a parking lot.

8:00 A.M. to 5:00 P.M.	$1 per $\frac{1}{2}$ hour
After 5:00 P.M.	$1 per hour

Mrs. Karlson parked her car from 1:30 P.M. to 7:00 P.M.
How much did she have to pay?

> The duration from 1:30 P.M. to 5:00 P.M. is $3\frac{1}{2}$ h.

Parking fee from 1:30 P.M. to 5:00 P.M. = $7
Parking fee from 5:00 P.M. to 7:00 P.M. = $2

Total parking fee = $

Mrs. Karlson had to pay $.

10. The workers in a factory are paid the following rates.

Weekdays	$28 per day
Saturdays and Sundays	$38 per day

Mr. Henderson worked from Friday to the following Tuesday.
How much was he paid?

> Mr. Henderson worked for 5 days.

Mr. Henderson's pay for 3 weekdays = $28 × 3
= $ ☐

Mr. Henderson's pay for Saturday and Sunday = $38 × 2
= $ ☐

Total pay = $ ☐

Mr. Henderson was paid $ ☐ .

11. The table shows the postage rates for sending magazines to another state.

Mass-step not over	Postage
20 g	$0.30
50 g	$0.40
100 g	$0.70
Per additional step of 100 g	$0.60

(a) Find the postage for a magazine with a mass of 85 g.

85 g is more than 50 g but less than 100 g.

Postage for 85 g = $ ⬚

The postage is $ ⬚ .

(b) Find the postage for a magazine with a mass of 330 g.

Postage for the 1st 100 g = $0.70

Postage for the next 230 g = $0.60 × 3

330 g is 230 g more than 100 g.

= $ ⬚

Total postage = $ ⬚

The postage is $ ⬚ .

12. The table shows the rates of charges for taxi fare in a city.

For the first km	$2.40
For every additional km	$0.40

Find the taxi fare for a trip of $5\frac{1}{2}$ km.

Fare for the 1st km = $2.40

Fare for the next $4\frac{1}{2}$ km = $0.40 × 5

= $ ⬚

Total fare = $ ⬚

The taxi fare for a trip of $5\frac{1}{2}$ km is $ ⬚.

Exercise 4, pages 153–154

1. If 7 pencils cost $1.50, how much do 35 pencils cost?

    (A) $2.00   (B) $4.50   (C) $5.90   (D) $7.50

2. A shoe factory produces 12,000 pairs of shoes a day.
    It is opened 5 days a week.
    How many pairs of shoes does it produce in 4 weeks?

    (A) 2,400   (B) 60,000   (C) 240,000   (D) 500,000

3. John is paid $60 for 8 hours of work.
    Tom is paid $8 per hour. What will be their total income from
    12 hours of work each?

    (A) $186   (B) $200   (C) $564   (D) $720

4. The rate for a taxi is $2.50 for the first mile, $2.70 for every mile or
    part of a mile after that, and $0.50 for each minute the driver waits.
    What is the closest estimate for the cost for an $8\frac{1}{2}$ mile trip in which
    the driver had to wait 8 minutes?

    (A) $10   (B) $20   (C) $30   (D) $40

5. Select True or False.

    A machine takes 35 minutes to fill 500 bottles.

    Its rate is $\frac{35}{500}$ bottles per minute.   True / False

6. Select True or False.

    A stapling machine that can staple 16 papers in
    20 seconds can staple 16 × 9 papers in 3 minutes.   True / False

7. A machine can print 50 similar pages per minute.
    At this rate, how long will it take to print 2,500 such pages?

8. A machine takes 4 minutes to seal 16 cookie boxes of the same kind.
    How many such cookie boxes can it seal in 1 minute?

9. Maggie's heart beats at the rate of 152 times every 2 minutes.
    At this rate, how many times does it beat in 30 minutes?

10. A pool is filled with water at the rate of 100 gal every 5 minutes. How long will it take to fill the pool with 1,000 gal of water?

11. At a fruit stand, oranges are sold at 5 for $2. How many oranges can Mr. King buy with $24?

12. A typist can type at a rate of 50 words per minute. How long will the typist take to type 4 pages each containing 300 words?

13. A copy machine can print at the rate of 90 similar copies every 5 minutes. How long will it take to print 270 such copies?

14. A machine caps 160 similar bottles every 2 minutes. At this rate, how long does it take to cap 400 bottles of the same kind?

15. How long will it take to fill an empty tank of capacity 200 gal if water flows into the tank at 8 gal per minute?

16. An empty rectangular tank measures 50 cm by 30 cm by 20 cm. It is to be filled with water from a tap.

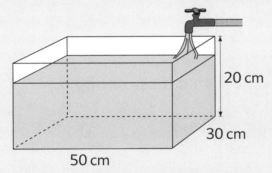

20 cm
30 cm
50 cm

(a) How many liters of water are needed to fill up the tank?
(b) If water flows from the tap at the rate of 12 L per minute, how long will it take to fill up the tank? (1 L = 1,000 cm³)

17. A pool is filled with water at the rate of 20 L per minute. How long will it take to fill the pool with 800 L of water?

18. The rates of charges for taxi fare in a city are shown in the table.

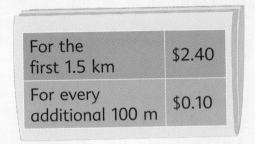

For the first 1.5 km	$2.40
For every additional 100 m	$0.10

Find the taxi fare for a journey of 4 km.

19. The table shows the postage rates for sending packages to Japan by air.

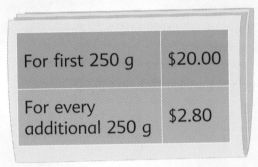

For first 250 g	$20.00
For every additional 250 g	$2.80

Find the postage for sending a package with a mass of 800 g.

20. Are all measurement conversions rate problems?
    Explain your answer.

 **Review 13, pages 155—158**

GLOSSARY

Word	Meaning
average	The total value of a set of data, divided by the number or frequency of that data.
coordinates	We can find any point on a graph by naming the **coordinates** of that point. These are ordered pairs of numbers. Example: Point A: (4, 2). The first number, 4, in (4, 2) is the x-coordinate. The second number, 2, is the y-coordinate.
graph	A (coordinate) graph has a horizontal and a vertical number line, called x-axis and y-axis respectively. The two lines intersect at the point (0, 0), called the origin.

Word	Meaning
rate	1. A quantity measured with respect to another measured quantity; e.g. a rate of speed of 60 miles an hour. 2. A measure of a part with respect to a whole; a proportion; e.g. the mortality rate; a tax rate. 3. The cost per unit of a commodity or service; e.g. postal rates.
sequence	An ordered list. Example: 1, 3, 5, 7 is a list of numbers that are in order and which are odd numbers.
term of a sequence	An element in the sequence. Example: 3 is the second term in the sequence 1, 3, 5, 7.

Grade 5 Curriculum Map

Common Core State Standards		Unit	Student Textbook Lessons	Student Workbook Exercises
OPERATIONS & ALGEBRAIC THINKING				
Write and interpret numerical expressions.				
5.OA.1	Use parentheses, brackets, or braces in numerical expressions, and evaluate expressions with these symbols.	**Unit 2 Lesson 1 Order of Operations**	**TB 5A:** 30–32	**WB 5A:** 30–32
5.OA.2	Write simple expressions that record calculations with numbers, and interpret numerical expressions without evaluating them. *For example, express the calculation "add 8 and 7, then multiply by 2" as 2 × (8 + 7). Recognize that 3 × (18932 + 921) is three times as large as 18932 + 921, without having to calculate the indicated sum or product.*	**Unit 2 Lesson 1 Order of Operations**	**TB 5A:** 33–34	**WB 5A:** 33–34
Analyze patterns and relationships.				
5.OA.3	Generate two numerical patterns using two given rules. Identify apparent relationships between corresponding terms. Form ordered pairs consisting of corresponding terms from the two patterns, and graph the ordered pairs on a coordinate plane. *For example, given the rule "Add 3" and the starting number 0, and given the rule "Add 6" and the starting number 0, generate terms in the resulting sequences, and observe that the terms in one sequence are twice the corresponding terms in the other sequence. Explain informally why this is so.*	**Unit 10 Lesson 4 Line Graphs**	**TB 5B:** 97–101	**WB 5B:** 79–83
NUMBER & OPERATIONS IN BASE TEN				
Understand the place-value system.				
5.NBT.1	Recognize that in a multi-digit number, a digit in one place represents 10 times as much as it represents in the place to its right and $\frac{1}{10}$ of what it represents in the place to its left.	**Unit 1 Lesson 1 Large Numbers** **Unit 1 Lesson 5 Multiplying by Tens, Hundreds or Thousands**	**TB 5A:** 8–9, 22, 24	**WB 5A:** 5–7, 18–20, 21–24

Common Core State Standards		Unit	Student Textbook Lessons	Student Workbook Exercises
		Unit 1 Lesson 6 Dividing by Tens, Hundreds or Thousands		
5.NBT.2	Explain patterns in the number of zeros of the product when multiplying a number by powers of 10, and explain patterns in the placement of the decimal point when a decimal is multiplied or divided by a power of 10. Use whole-number exponents to denote powers of 10.	**Unit 1 Lesson 5 Multiplying by Tens, Hundreds or Thousands** **Unit 7 Lesson 5 Multiplication by Tens, Hundreds, or Thousands** **Unit 7 Lesson 6 Division by Tens, Hundreds, or Thousands**	**TB 5A:** 22–23 **TB 5B:** 28–35	**WB 5A:** 18–20 **WB 5B:** 46–48
5.NBT.3a	Read, write, and compare decimals to thousandths. Read and write decimals to thousandths using base-ten numerals, number names, and expanded form, e.g., $347.392 = 3 \times 100 + 4 \times 10 + 7 \times 1 + 3 \times \left(\frac{1}{10}\right) + 9 \times \left(\frac{1}{100}\right) + 2 \times \left(\frac{1}{1000}\right)$.	**Unit 7 Lesson 1 Tenths, Hundredths and Thousandths**	**TB 5B:** 8–11	**WB 5B:** 5–6
5.NBT.3b	Read, write, and compare decimals to thousandths. Compare two decimals to thousandths based on meanings of the digits in each place, using >, =, and < symbols to record the results of comparisons.	**Unit 7 Lesson 1 Tenths, Hundredths and Thousandths**	**TB 5B:** 12	**WB 5B:** 7

Common Core State Standards		Unit	Student Textbook Lessons	Student Workbook Exercises
5.NBT.4	Use place value understanding to round decimals to any place.	**Unit 7 Lesson 2 Approximation** **Unit 7 Lesson 3 Add and Subtract Decimals** **Unit 7 Lesson 4 Multiply and Divide Decimals by a 1-Digit Whole Number**	**TB 5B:** 14–16, 18, 21, 24–25	**WB 5B:** 8–9, 12–14
Perform operations with multi-digit whole numbers and with decimals to hundredths.				
5.NBT.5	Fluently multiply multi-digit whole numbers using the standard algorithm.	**Unit 2 Lesson 4 Multiplication by a 2-Digit Whole Number**	**TB 5A:** 44–46	**WB 5A:** **48–50**
5.NBT.6	Find whole-number quotients of whole numbers with up to four-digit dividends and two-digit divisors, using strategies based on place value, the properties of operations, and/or the relationship between multiplication and division. Illustrate and explain the calculation by using equations, rectangular arrays, and/or area models.	**Unit 2 Lesson 5 Division by a 2-Digit Whole Number**	**TB 5A:** 47–53	**WB 5A:** 51–55
5.NBT.7	Add, subtract, multiply, and divide decimals to hundredths, using concrete models or drawings and strategies based on place value, properties of operations, and/or the relationship between addition and subtraction; relate the strategy to a written method and explain the reasoning used.	**Unit 7 Lesson 3 Add and Subtract Decimals** **Unit 7 Lesson 4 Multiply and Divide Decimals by a 1-Digit Whole Number**	**TB 5B:** 17–23, 28–35, 40–52	**WB 5B:** 9–13, 17–22, 29–39

Common Core State Standards		Unit	Student Textbook Lessons	Student Workbook Exercises
		Unit 7 Lesson 5 Multiplication by Tens, Hundreds or Thousands		
		Unit 7 Lesson 6 Division by Tens, Hundreds or Thousands		
		Unit 8 Lesson 1 Multiplication by a 2-Digit Whole Number		
		Unit 8 Lesson 2 Division by a 2-Digit Whole Number		
		Unit 8 Lesson 3 Multiplication by a Decimal		
		Unit 8 Lesson 4 Division by a Decimal		
NUMBER AND OPERATIONS – FRACTIONS				
Use equivalent fractions as a strategy to add and subtract fractions.				
5.NF.1	Add and subtract fractions with unlike denominators (including mixed numbers) by replacing given fractions with equivalent fractions in such a way as to produce an equivalent sum or difference of fractions with like denominators. *For example, $\frac{2}{3} + \frac{5}{4} = \frac{8}{12} + \frac{15}{12} = \frac{23}{12}$. (In general, $\frac{a}{b} + \frac{c}{d} = \frac{(ad + bc)}{bd}$.)*	**Unit 3 Lesson 3 Addition and Subtraction of Unlike Fractions** **Unit 3 Lesson 4 Addition and Subtraction of Mixed Numbers**	**TB 5A:** 67–74	**WB 5A:** 69–76

Common Core State Standards		Unit	Student Textbook Lessons	Student Workbook Exercises
5.NF.2	Solve word problems involving addition and subtraction of fractions referring to the same whole, including cases of unlike denominators, e.g., by using visual fraction models or equations to represent the problem. Use benchmark fractions and number sense of fractions to estimate mentally and assess the reasonableness of answers. *For example, recognize an incorrect result $\frac{2}{5} + \frac{1}{2} = \frac{3}{7}$, by observing that $\frac{3}{7} < \frac{1}{2}$.*	**Unit 3 Lesson 3 Addition and Subtraction of Unlike Fractions** **Unit 3 Lesson 4 Addition and Subtraction of Mixed Numbers**	**TB 5A:** 75–76	**WB 5A:** 77–79
Apply and extend previous understandings of multiplication and division.				
5.NF.3	Interpret a fraction as division of the numerator by the denominator $\left(\frac{a}{b} = a \div b\right)$. Solve word problems involving division of whole numbers leading to answers in the form of fractions or mixed numbers, e.g., by using visual fraction models or equations to represent the problem. *For example, interpret $\frac{3}{4}$ as the result of dividing 3 by 4, noting that $\frac{3}{4}$ multiplied by 4 equals 3, and that when 3 wholes are shared equally among 4 people each person has a share of size $\frac{3}{4}$. If 9 people want to share a 50-pound sack of rice equally by weight, how many pounds of rice should each person get? Between what two whole numbers does your answer lie?*	**Unit 3 Lesson 2 Fractions and Division** **Unit 3 Lesson 4 Addition and Subtraction of Mixed Numbers**	**TB 5A:** 63–66, 72–76	**WB 5A:** 66–68, 73–79
5.NF.4a	Apply and extend previous understandings of multiplication to multiply a fraction or whole number by a fraction. Interpret the product $\left(\frac{a}{b}\right) \times q$ as a parts of a partition of q into b equal parts; equivalently, as the result of a sequence of operations $a \times q \div b$. *For example, use a visual fraction model to show $\left(\frac{2}{3}\right) \times 4 = \frac{8}{3}$, and create a story context for this equation. Do the same with $\left(\frac{2}{3}\right) \times \left(\frac{4}{5}\right) = \frac{8}{15}$. (In general, $\left(\frac{a}{b}\right) \times \left(\frac{c}{d}\right) = \frac{ac}{bd}$.)*	**Unit 4 Lesson 1 Product of Fractions**	**TB 5A:** 91–94	**WB 5A:** 97–101

Common Core State Standards		Unit	Student Textbook Lessons	Student Workbook Exercises
5.NF.4b	Apply and extend previous understandings of multiplication to multiply a fraction or whole number by a fraction. Find the area of a rectangle with fractional side lengths by tiling it with unit squares of the appropriate unit fraction side lengths, and show that the area is the same as would be found by multiplying the side lengths. Multiply fractional side lengths to find areas of rectangles, and represent fraction products as rectangular areas.	Unit 5 Lesson 1 Square Units	TB 5A: 126–128	WB 5A: 139–140
5.NF.5a	Interpret multiplication as scaling (resizing), by: Comparing the size of a product to the size of one factor on the basis of the size of the other factor, without performing the indicated multiplication.	Unit 4 Lesson 5 Product of a Fraction and Whole Number	TB 5A: 77–78, 83	WB 5A: 80–81, 85–86
5.NF.5b	Interpret multiplication as scaling (resizing), by: Explaining why multiplying a given number by a fraction greater than 1 results in a product greater than the given number (recognizing multiplication by whole numbers greater than 1 as a familiar case); explaining why multiplying a given number by a fraction less than 1 results in a product smaller than the given number; and relating the principle of fraction equivalence $\frac{a}{b} = \frac{(n \times a)}{(n \times b)}$ to the effect of multiplying $\frac{a}{b}$ by 1.	Unit 4 Lesson 5 Product of a Fraction and Whole Number	TB 5A: 98	WB 5A: 106–109
5.NF.6	Solve real world problems involving multiplication of fractions and mixed numbers, e.g., by using visual fraction models or equations to represent the problem.	Unit 3 Lesson 6 Word Problems	TB 5A: 85–87	WB 5A: 87–91
5.NF.7a	Apply and extend previous understandings of division to divide unit fractions by whole numbers and whole numbers by unit fractions. Interpret division of a unit fraction by a non-zero whole number, and compute such quotients. *For example, create a story context for $\left(\frac{1}{3}\right) \div 4$, and use a visual fraction model to show the quotient. Use the relationship between multiplication and division to explain that $\left(\frac{1}{3}\right) \div 4 = \frac{1}{12}$ because $\left(\frac{1}{12}\right) \times 4 = \frac{1}{3}$.*	Unit 4 Lesson 3 Dividing a Fraction by a Whole Number	TB 5A: 99–102	WB 5A: 110–116

Common Core State Standards		Unit	Student Textbook Lessons	Student Workbook Exercises
5.NF.7b	Apply and extend previous understandings of division to divide unit fractions by whole numbers and whole numbers by unit fractions. Interpret division of a whole number by a unit fraction, and compute such quotients. *For example, create a story context for $4 \div \left(\frac{1}{5}\right)$, and use a visual fraction model to show the quotient. Use the relationship between multiplication and division to explain that $4 \div \left(\frac{1}{5}\right) = 20$ because $20 \times \left(\frac{1}{5}\right) = 4$.*	**Unit 4 Lesson 4 Dividing by a Fraction**	**TB 5A:** 103–111	**WB 5A:** 117–122
5.NF.7c	Apply and extend previous understandings of division to divide unit fractions by whole numbers and whole numbers by unit fractions. Solve real world problems involving division of unit fractions by non-zero whole numbers and division of whole numbers by unit fractions, e.g., by using visual fraction models and equations to represent the problem. *For example, how much chocolate will each person get if 3 people share $\frac{1}{2}$ lb of chocolate equally? How many $\frac{1}{3}$-cup servings are in 2 cups of raisins?*	**Unit 4 Lesson 4 Dividing by a Fraction** **Unit 4 Lesson 5 More Word Problems**	**TB 5A:** 108, 113	**WB 5A:** 121, 123–127
MEASUREMENT AND DATA				
Convert like measurement units within a given measurement system.				
5.MD.1	Convert among different-sized standard measurement units within a given measurement system (e.g., convert 5 cm to 0.05 m), and use these conversions in solving multi-step, real world problems.	**Unit 8 Lesson 5 Conversion of Measures**	**TB 5B:** 53–56	**WB 5B:** 41–42
Represent and interpret data.				
5.MD.2	Make a line plot to display a data set of measurements in fractions of a unit $\left(\frac{1}{2}, \frac{1}{4}, \frac{1}{8}\right)$. Use operations on fractions for this grade to solve problems involving information presented in line plots. *For example, given different measurements of liquid in identical beakers, find the amount of liquid each beaker would contain if the total amount in all the beakers were redistributed equally.*	**Unit 10 Lesson 2 Line Plots**	**TB 5B:** 89–90	**WB 5B:** 73–74

Common Core State Standards		Unit	Student Textbook Lessons	Student Workbook Exercises
Geometric measurement: understand concepts of volume.				
5.MD.3a	Recognize volume as an attribute of solid figures and understand concepts of volume measurement. A cube with side length 1 unit, called a "unit cube," is said to have "one cubic unit" of volume, and can be used to measure volume.	**Unit 9 Lesson 1 Cubic Units**	**TB 5B:** 63	**WB 5B:** 46–48
5.MD.3b	Recognize volume as an attribute of solid figures and understand concepts of volume measurement. A solid figure which can be packed without gaps or overlaps using *n* unit cubes is said to have a volume of *n* cubic units.	**Unit 9 Lesson 1 Cubic Units**	**TB 5B:** 63	**WB 5B:** 46–48
5.MD.4	Measure volumes by counting unit cubes, using cubic cm, cubic in, cubic ft, and improvised units.	**Unit 9 Lesson 1 Cubic Units**	**TB 5B:** 64	**WB 5B:** 46–48
5.MD.5a	Relate volume to the operations of multiplication and addition and solve real world and mathematical problems involving volume. Find the volume of a right rectangular prism with whole-number side lengths by packing it with unit cubes, and show that the volume is the same as would be found by multiplying the edge lengths, equivalently by multiplying the height by the area of the base. Represent threefold whole-number products as volumes, e.g., to represent the associative property of multiplication.	**Unit 9 Lesson 2 Volume of Rectangular Prisms**	**TB 5B:** 65	**WB 5B:** 49
5.MD.5b	Relate volume to the operations of multiplication and addition and solve real world and mathematical problems involving volume. Apply the formulas $V = l \times w \times h$ and $V = b \times h$ for rectangular prisms to find volumes of right rectangular prisms with whole-number edge lengths in the context of solving real world and mathematical problems.	**Unit 9 Lesson 2 Volume of Rectangular Prisms** **Unit 9 Lesson 3 Finding the Volume of a Solid**	**TB 5B:** 65–68, 72–78	**WB 5B:** 49–50, 54–60

Common Core State Standards		Unit	Student Textbook Lessons	Student Workbook Exercises
5.MD.5c	Relate volume to the operations of multiplication and addition and solve real world and mathematical problems involving volume. Recognize volume as additive. Find volumes of solid figures composed of two non-overlapping right rectangular prisms by adding the volumes of the non-overlapping parts, applying this technique to solve real world problems.	**Unit 9 Lesson 2 Volume of Rectangular Prisms**	**TB 5B:** 69–71	**WB 5B:** 51–53
GEOMETRY				
Graph points on the coordinate plane to solve real-world and mathematical problems.				
5.G.1	Use a pair of perpendicular number lines, called axes, to define a coordinate system, with the intersection of the lines (the origin) arranged to coincide with the 0 on each line and a given point in the plane located by using an ordered pair of numbers, called its coordinates. Understand that the first number indicates how far to travel from the origin in the direction of one axis, and the second number indicates how far to travel in the direction of the second axis, with the convention that the names of the two axes and the coordinates correspond (e.g., x-axis and x-coordinate, y-axis and y-coordinate).	**Unit 10 Lesson 3 Coordinate Graphs**	**TB 5B:** 92–95	**WB 5B:** 75–77
5.G.2	Represent real world and mathematical problems by graphing points in the first quadrant of the coordinate plane, and interpret coordinate values of points in the context of the situation.	**Unit 10 Lesson 3 Coordinate Graphs**	**TB 5B:** 102–105	**WB 5B:** 84–89
Classify two-dimensional figures into categories based on their properties.				
5.G.3	Understand that attributes belonging to a category of two-dimensional figures also belong to all subcategories of that category. For example, all rectangles have four right angles and squares are rectangles, so all squares have four right angles.	**Unit 11 Lesson 1 Looking Back**	**TB 5B:** 117–118	**WB 5B:** 102–104
5.G.4	Classify two-dimensional figures in a hierarchy based on properties.	**Unit 11 Lesson 1 Looking Back**	**TB 5B:** 119	**WB 5B:** 102–104

Index